E257

may be

✓ S0-AYB-664

Christopher Hollis

June 2. 1969

Friction

With Love, Peter

Christopher Hollis also has written

DR. JOHNSON

THE AMERICAN HERESY

THE MONSTROUS REGIMENT

DRYDEN

ERASMUS

ST. IGNATIUS

THOMAS MORE

TWO NATIONS: A FINANCIAL STUDY

THE BREAKDOWN OF MONEY

FOREIGNERS AREN'T FOOLS

FOREIGNERS AREN'T KNAVES

LENIN

ITALY IN AFRICA

DEATH OF A GENTLEMAN

FOSSETT'S MEMORY

CHRISTOPHER HOLLIS

With Love, Peter

02768

PR
6015
.0413
W5

PR6015.H72W5   ST. JOSEPH'S UNIVERSITY   STX
With love, Peter.

3 9353 00020 9161

THE DECLAN X. McMULLEN COMPANY, INC.

COPYRIGHT 1948

The Declan X. McMullen Company, Inc.

PRINTED IN THE U.S.A.

TO
MONICA

Preface

My sister Ruth and I were twins. Our father was a Scots businessman and our mother came from Kentucky. We were the great-grandchildren of a Confederate general of the American Civil War. I have always fancied that the Kentucky strain in us had far more influence on our characters than the Scots. Perhaps it was only that that which was the more strange was the more noticeable. Between two strains, the one of which is foreign and the other native to the place of one's upbringing, it is perhaps natural that the foreign strain is the more evident—both to oneself and to others. We were brought up in England, and to be the son of a Scots businessman in England is nothing very odd. Confederate generals are rarer. Besides, the Civil War has a quality unique among wars in capturing the imagination. I have lived now through the two greatest wars in history—lost in them friends, relations, a wife—seen powers and empires crumble, and yet that which I have seen and felt can never be quite so real to me as the memory of my great-grandfather marching up into Maryland with Lee and standing beside him on the day of Appomatox.

> *The tyrant's heel is on thy shore*
> *Maryland, my Maryland*

is still my national anthem, and the crime that I find it most hard to forgive the Communists is their theft of the consecrated tune for their own Red Flag. There are many hundreds of thousands like me, scattered through the Southern States. Yet, it is a strange nostalgia indeed, for, when questioned, we cannot in the last analysis even say that it would have been a good thing if the South had won the war and effected her secession, and I, at any rate, have never had much sympathy with that merely negative lack of progress which is to-day the South's most noticeable characteristic.

It was after the Civil War that my mother's family moved west from Virginia into Kentucky. All Southerners pretend that they are very aristocratic. The truth is different. Most of us are really "poor white trash" enough. In fact, my great-grandfather's name was Preserved Fish—Fish because that was his name, and Preserved because, at his baptism, he fell head foremost into the font and was only hoiked out just in time. He was a Primitive Methodist. It always seemed to me an odd name. Certainly it was not an aristocratic one. But ancestral pride is built largely on the virtues of geometrical progression. If you go back far enough, you have a large number of ancestors, and, in a fecund, vigorous, not too particular society, at least one of them, legitimate or illegitimate, is pretty sure to have been a gentleman. There is no need to talk about the others. So one of our ancestors was a collateral of Randolph of Roanoke—that strange, impotent, most powerful master who boasted that he "loved justice and hated equality"—the stormy rebel before whom the panorama of a generation passed in delirium on that terrifying deathbed in the house of "one Badger" in North Third Street, Philadelphia. He died like a character in an Elizabethan play, and that is more than can be said for most American politicians.

My grandmother had the tale of Randolph's death-bed from Dr. Parish, the Quaker doctor, who attended him and who went back home immediately afterward and wrote down all that Randolph had said. Randolph had lived his life again in his delirium, had talked of Clay and Calhoun, of Andrew Jackson and the Emperor of Russia. Then, as is the habit of the dying, he had wandered back to his youth, to Jefferson, to his Negroes, to his brother Dicky, to his mother. He was out on the hills with his dogs above Bizarre, and, when death came to him, he was a boy again, fleeing over the Virginian mountains to the distant boom of the English guns of Cornwallis on the march to Yorktown. It is in such stories that the history of the South lives on to-day, and he who has ever heard them can never be deaf to the past.

Yet, we were brought up in England, with Kentucky only as a memory and a place for summer visits. I went to Eton, left just in time to do a few months at a cadet school before the end of the first war, went up to Oxford, got a third, went into the motor business, played a good deal of cricket, ate, drank, and, in time, married more happily than I deserved and begot a family. Thus were the twenty years between the wars filled up. During those same years my sister had married Bobby Fossett and had become the mother of his three children and the mistress of his home at Barston, in Somerset. With the war, both Bobby and I joined up—he for the last stand at Calais and a soldier's grave, I for an inglorious desk at the War Office, varied only with trips hardly less inglorious round the Mediterranean and well behind the battleline. It was the crowning ignominy of my war that it brought greater danger to my wife than it did to me. She was killed by a German bomb in one of the worst raids of the Battle of London.

It is well known that there is commonly a mysterious and telepathic sympathy between twins—and this sympathy is, perhaps, most strong when the twins are of different sexes. Now, between my sister and me, the bond of sympathy, though strong, had not been simple. It had not meant, by any means, that we held identical opinions. To the contrary. My sister accepted from the first the strong influence of her husband and accepted, although to reinterpret, his opinions.

In politics they were what I would call Tories rather than Conservatives. He was a member, but a critical member, of the Conservative party of his day. His true faith was one of a profound acceptance of human equality in fundamentals, combined with an equally profound belief that a hierarchical organisation was the organisation which alone could bring happiness to man. He was quite without personal ambition, and it was of complete indifference to him what position in society he might be called on to occupy. Like the creature of the catechism, he was prepared "to do his duty in that state of life into which it should please God to call him." Who was up and who was down was, to his mind, secondary. It was important that the matter should be settled, and that all energy should not be dissipated in a universal scramble. To schemes of social reform he was whimsically indifferent. He did not think that any of them would do much good, but, on the other hand, he thought that their opponents often exaggerated their harm. In the day of the breaking of nations the rich must be prepared to lose their riches and to resign their privileges. New presbyter, it is true, was unlikely to be an improvement on old priest, but the value was in the example of ready sacrifice.

My sister shared these opinions, differing only in that she spent less time in discussing the theoretical bases of a society, which, in any event, were by definition indifferent, and more in the practical business of farming.

So, too, with religion. Bobby was a very clear-headed and well-informed Christian, conscious that there was an inherent mystery in all existence to which the Christian religion alone provided a key, ready, at all times, to give an account of the faith that was in him, possibly a little bit too contemptuous of those who rejected or failed to notice the mystery. He was a Protestant—not in the sense of having anti-Catholic prejudices—but in the sense that the ethical and metaphysical aspects of religion attracted him, rather than the sacramental or the mystical. His greatest friend was an old schoolfellow, a parson, George Borthwick, a man of high virtue and high intelligence, but, like Bobby himself, a metaphysician and less than Bobby of a poet. I have never met anyone who knew the answers to all the questions better than George—and that is a high virtue—but I could not help feeling that he was sometimes a little too confident in them. Bobby was slightly less dogmatic, but of the same bias. As he used to say, "I would have been a very good Calvinist, if only the Calvinists were right." He meant that he liked the rationalistic way in which the Calvinists attacked the problems of religion, but he thought their particular arguments fallacious. My sister was much more naturally, even as she was much less rationally, religious than her husband. She was a seventeenth-century High Churchwoman—something out of Bemerton.

Now, in contrast to all that, I was throughout all the years between the two wars little better than a barlounger. I avoided the more savage and flagrant vices, but on analysis I should hesitate to boast that even there I avoided them because of repugnance at their viciousness. It was rather that in an easy, indolent good nature I disliked being disliked. I shrank from making myslf odious— which is not a very high motive. If I have never been able to understand the tyrants and torturers of this world, it is not that I have been unable to understand their temptations and their wickedness. I have all too much precedent to teach me how fatally easy it is to sin from indolence and self-indulgence, how easy, perhaps, to cause suffering to others, so long as it happens incidentally and round the corner and one can shut one's eyes to what is happening. But it is my weakness more than my strength that I could never stand face to face with a man and win his hatred just to satisfy my own lust. All my so-called opinions of those years—left-wing politics and crude agnosticisms—were, in truth, more habits of social speech than opinions, ready to be sloughed off, as such habits are, at the first touch of reality and of suffering.

Only two claims would I make for myself at this time. First, I never lost my faith in the poets. Second, in a curious, confused way my agnosticism was shot through with a sense of what religion was about and, so to speak, how it ought to work, deeper—dare I say, without too gross a spiritual pride?—than that of many men and women, a thousand times better, more spiritual and more orthodox than I. That is to say, which key fitted the lock, what was the truth, I still was all uncertain. But I did always remember that "all things go out into mystery," that religion was a poem long before it was an ethical code, and that, even though there was no Grail to find, the most practical of all quests—indeed, the only truly practical quest—was the search for the Holy Grail. Thomas More says somewhere that no true Christian should ever take the Resurrection for granted. He should never cease to be as surprised at it as were the first women who went to the tomb on the first Easter morning. I think I can claim that I have always thought this sense. At a time when I thought the whole story nonsense, I thought that this was the only way in which it could be sense. The Gospel is good news, and, even when it is old, historically, it must still be new, artistically—have still about it that stab of surprise which Aristotle so rightly insisted was a requisite of all great art.

How great a man was Aristotle!

But, having said that, I have said all that there is to

13

be said for myself. It is only right that I do not pitch my claims any higher. For, in the years of the first letters in this book—in the early years of the war—I am conscious that my mind, already in motion as, indeed, it still is to this day, was both far less formed and far less sensible than it would appear from these letters. These letters pretend to no absolute consistency. As is but natural, moods, often slightly in contradiction of one another, succeed from letter to letter, but there is a greater approximation to consistency in the letters than would have been found from a record of my conversations over the same period. I discover this from reading them, and the reasons, I fancy, are these: I think that I probably always have written and spoken more sensibly and responsibly to my sister than to other people. Partly, that is because, in general, one does always tend to talk more sensibly to the sensible and to be ashamed to air before them the folly that one parades so easily before the fool. Partly, it was, in particular, the effect of that strange, telepathic sympathy of twins, which caused my sister and me, speaking perhaps in different languages when we spoke to other people, to some extent to merge our personalities and our opinions—to move towards each other and to seek to speak with a common voice when we spoke to each other. Twins are the creatures of a mysterious destiny, which compels two souls to go forward hand in hand through the jungle, whether they wish it so or whether they do not.

There was another great difference between us, resulting, in part, from circumstances, in part, perhaps, from temperament. I have always had an intellectual sympathy with the faith that gives a primacy to agriculture over all the other economic activities of man. Nineteenth-century utilitarianism, which would produce in a country whatever it was immediately cheapest to produce, which cared nothing whether it grew its food at home or gained it by the exchange of manufactured goods for the food of other nations, always seemed to me a bloodless folly. Cities, indeed, and industry there must be—alike for cultural as for economic reasons—but there is all the difference in the world between the Greek ideas of a city fed from its surrounding countryside and the modern conception of the vast metropolis devouring its own hinterlands and dependent on the fluctuating chances of commerce to draw its food indifferently from every corner of the world.

I have a degree of sympathy with modern talk against privilege. It is to the advantage neither of society nor of the individual that a youth should be born with the proverbial silver spoon in his mouth and be sheltered from birth from every one of the buffetings of fortune, by which his normal fellows are assailed. Yet, life is more than the adventure of one generation. Incomparably the greater part of the great achievements of man have been the achievements neither of the exceptionally privileged nor of the wholly unprivileged, but of men and women of the middle class, the children of parents who have been able to win for them a certain advantage of birth and education. Freaks and sports, who flash up into distinction, coming no man knows whence and departing no man knows whither, have generally been a disruptive influence in society, and society would have been the better without their distinction. The career should be open, but not wide open, to talents, or—if you prefer to put it so—the talent to rule is rarely found save among those who have been trained to rule. So, although inventions which change the material habits of life are in themselves good, and, indeed, cannot be prevented, whether they be good or bad, yet it is, as sad experience has taught us, a misfortune for society when inventions crowd in on one another too rapidly—so rapidly that the son is tempted to think that his life is quite of a different kind from that of his father, so changed are its accidents. We are, in truth, each one of us, but a link in a chain, a chain which stretches back through our ancestors into the impenetrable past, and which will stretch on through our descendants into the yet more impenetrable future. Of all democratic doctrines the most truly and deeply democratic is that which refuses to confine itself to taking the opinions of those who suffer from the arbitrary accident of living, but which pays equal regard to the traditional opinion of mankind—which does not disdain to poll the franchise of the dead.

All this I always believed up to a point—even in the days when I combined such belief with many follies contradictory to it. I have come of late years to believe it most firmly. Yet, it was as a philosopher that I believed it. It was a theory to me. Broken from my Kentucky roots, mouldering in the Midlands, where no man truly lives, I came to value stability through horror at the absence of it, much as, I fear, I came to value virtue through horror at the absence of it. Neither in virtue nor in stability was mine to be considered any *anima naturaliter Christiana.*

Now, fortune and temperament combined to give to my sister Ruth a happier fate. She married into stability, and she had a character apt to embrace good at its own aspect and not in mere recoil from the opposite of it. It came natural to her to play the part of her husband's wife, to live the country life, to be the link in the chain, inheriting and bequeathing, and, because she lived and breathed the air, she troubled her mind the less, save under challenge, about the theory of it. My approval of her way of life before the war was to some extent an idle and a theoretical approval. Then, after her husband's death, she appealed to me to help her with her life and the upbringing of her children—an appeal which no one, and, least of all, a twin brother, could have refused. There followed my own wife's death in the Battle of London, and, after they had returned from America, my children went to live with hers at Barston. The two bereaved families became, as it were, a joint family—as I hope that they will forever remain—and the relationship of circumstance made even abnormally intimate the closest of all relationships of blood. I was working—usually at the War Office, sometimes for brief trips round the Mediterranean—but Barston became more passionately a home to me than most men in this homeless, nomad age have ever owned. Every moment that I could snatch from London I spent there, and the children of both families became common children whom we shared together.

Martin finished his time at Trumpinghurst, passed thence to Oxford, to the army, to an O.C.T.U., to Africa

17

and the M.C., to an Italian prison-camp, and finally to Greece. Margaret was in and out of a convent school and, thence, to a Government department and an engagement to Michael Paravane. Robert followed in his father's footsteps to Eton, where the war's end still found him.

There was a great fallacy that vitiated the many truths in the Cobdenite theory that the end of all economic activity was the cheapest possible production. Of course, there was much truth in this theory, and it was right to invoke it against merely obstinate conservatism. It is a mere tautology to say that improvements are desirable, but it is a dangerous delusion to say that the immediately cheapest production on the short term is necessarily the best production. You can use the machine in such a way as to destroy it, and, if this be true of the factory, it is yet more true of the field. The final loyalty must be to the land. The aim of the farmer must be, not only to produce good crops, but also to leave the land in as good a condition as he found it. That is why agriculture has never prospered, save in a society which valued highly the institution of the family, and why wise policy has found it best that land should normally be held by hereditary transmission. The surest of all tests, both of wisdom and of virtue, is the planting of trees—the sowing of a seed that can be enjoyed only by one's children. Farming without the family—farming without a belief in hereditary transmission and the stable life—leads, as we have seen, only to the dust bowl. But to my sister Ruth all these truths were self-evident. At Barston the farm was the bond of the family, and the family existed as a guarantee that farming should aim at more than the passing prosperity of the day.

It is often said that agriculture is more than an industry; it is a way of life. It is perhaps more often said than its meaning is defined. There are two senses, I fancy, in which it is true, or in which at least it ought to be true. First, there is not on the farm that rigid division between play and work which we find in the office or the factory. In office and factory, at one definite minute one goes to work, and at another definite minute one leaves work. Life dances to the clock and to the hooter. The farmer lives among his work. He is never entirely off duty, and at the same time every day he does many things of which it would be impossible to say with certainty whether they were work or play. Secondly, in the old days the village was not merely a working unit; it was also a playing unit —a social unit. I have no wish to idealise the old squires and landlords. The moral justification for a squirearchy is that a few families should have somewhat more money, somewhat better facilities for entertainment, than their neighbours, that their children should go away from home to receive their education in a wider world, that in maturity their members should still mix on one business or another with that wider world, but all for a purpose. It is all that they may bring that breath of a wider world into the lives of their more restricted neighbours. In every generation of English history there have been some squires who lived a life in which their privileges were thus accepted as a vocation, and others who accepted privilege merely as a boon to be selfishly enjoyed.

The years before the war had brought a new threat, for better or for worse, to village life. The increased ease of communications had enabled first the rich, and afterward the poor, to move more easily about the country and to take their pleasure, as opportunity offered, far from home. This had doubtless advantages, but it had one overriding and enormous disadvantage. The greatest evil of big towns is that the population segregates itself into what the modern jargon calls income groups. In the village this is impossible. If you want to play with people of your own income or of your own tastes or interests, then you cannot play at all; but, if the county becomes the social unit, as it was tending to become before the war, then, in the country, as in the city, people seek out companions of their own income and their own graduated amusements.

The war, therefore, with all its inconveniences, brought to the village life a great compensating advantage. Social life suffered from the absence of the young and from all the shortages of wartime austerity, but, at least, it gained by being driven in upon itself. The Home Guard, whether or not it performed a military service, at least performed a great social service. It compelled people of different sorts to get to know one another. How can one be better compelled to get to know a man than by watching with him through the night? And petrol rationing drove the new generation back again to the habits of its grandparents and compelled the villagers once more to find their social amenities in one another's company. Men and women who, in past years, had come to think a weekly trip to the town cinema a necessity of life now rediscovered the amusement of the village concert, the village drama and even the village brains-trust.

I think that I can fairly boast, both for myself and for my sister, that this suited us very well. In this sad world I have found many a cause for sorrow, but, on the other hand, it has been one of my compensations that many of the things of which others complain most bitterly have never been to me cause of suffering at all. I have never been greatly troubled by the fear of danger, much as I admire courage. Similarly, on a smaller scale, it is almost a convention of English life to complain of the boredom of the social duties and to count it as the main joy of life when somebody or other goes. I do not know if it is our American blood, but both Ruth and I are by nature and taste "good mixers," and all these social occasions, that are, it seems, so great a weariness to so many, were always, alike to Ruth, to me, and to the children of both of us, occasions of delight.

Such few formal dances as I have ever attended I have always found intensely boring, but the Barston village dances were the greatest fun. As far as I recollect, the hired band always broke down on the way, but it never mattered in the least. Armstrong, the inn-keeper, operated an old phonograph with six records, which, by the end of the war, had been reduced to five; when people got tired of dancing to them, Margaret struck valiantly at such notes on the old piano as were at all respondent and Martin accompanied her on a concertina. The more sedate dances were soon abandoned in favour of the more boisterous follies of Paul Jones, in which it was Robert's main ambition to dance with Bertha, the very aged cook. "Don't squeeze me, Master Robert; you mustn't squeeze me like that," she would giggle with all the vigour of a yet hopeful seventy-five. At last, midnight would be ushered in, on Ruth's insistence, to the strains of Okey-Pokey:

> *Your right leg up*
> *And your right leg back*
> *And twirl it all about;*
> *And you do the okey-pokey*
> *And you turn right 'round*
> *And that's what it's all about,*
> > *Oy,*
> *And the smoke goes up the chimney just the same.*

Nothing is more tiresome than the trumpetings of paternal pride. That is why I have written a book that is, after a manner, about my sister's children, but nothing would induce me to write a book about my own children. Yet, I think that they culled from this atmosphere a kind irresponsibility of high spirits, which is, within limits, attractive in the young.

"Isn't that the telephone?" asked Ruth one day, vainly attempting to hear above the surrounding din.

"No," incomprehensibly replied my Christopher, "it's the cow's dinner."

Or again, when I was one day proposing to give a talk on the wireless:

"Your father's going to talk on the wireless," said Ruth.

"He can't," said Christopher. "He's too big."

But I hope that they have learnt more than that. The virtue of high spirits and the vice of low spirits seem to me both commonly underestimated. "There is no duty," says Stevenson, "which we so commonly neglect as the duty of being happy." The maxim is cast in a violently paradoxical form, which robs it of meaning. The duty that we neglect is the duty of being cheerful and high-spirited, and we have the highest of Christian warrant for it that that is, indeed, a duty. False *bonhomie* is, indeed, no virtue, but what is that but to say that every virtue has its hypocrisy? Or again, that in this, as in all virtues, the limits of freedom are hard to know and some people are doubtless afflicted with low spirits and melancholy as a disease? They are to be pitied, but not to be praised. I am glad that my children should grow up in an atmosphere where moods are not pandered to and where cheerfulness is demanded.

With Love, Peter

1

My dear Ruth,

Well, so here it is—after all our talk and hopes and wishful drinking. You remember Browning's Englishman in Italy and Italian in England? The Italian in England talks about nothing except Italian politics, as if nobody could possibly be interested in anything else. The Englishman in Italy talks about the weather and the pomegranates and the butterflies. At the end he has a passing feeling that perhaps there are more important things in life, but it never occurs to him that anything in Italy—anything going on around him—could be more important. The only important things in the world are the things that happen in England.

> *"Such trifles," you say?*
> *In England, at home*
> *Men meet gravely to-day*
> *And debate if abolishing Corn Laws*
> *Be righteous and wise—*
> *If 'twere proper, Scirocco should vanish*
> *In black from the skies.*

Well, Scirocco has not vanished in black from the skies, and, for the moment, all the world in which my mind has been moving—what I might call the world of Huxtable ploughs—looks very small, indeed, and foolish. And yet, I do not know. It may be that Huxtable ploughs will be the one thing that will survive out of this war. Something must survive, and no one can tell what, but it is as likely to be Huxtable ploughs as anything else. If we cannot prevent landslides on Exmoor, what can we prevent?

Having been wrong about everything up to now, I will not start being wrong all over again and regale you with a series of prophecies, first-hand or second-hand, about how long the war is going to last. Besides, you know what Bobby thinks about it, and his thoughts, even when we differ, are more important than mine. Even when I believe him to be wrong, I know that he has better reasons for being wrong than I have for being right. But I must confess that the result of my talk with him has been to leave me profoundly worried. Up till then I had just been an ordinary Englishman about the war.

Question: Were we right to fight?

Answer: What else could we do?

Question: What are we fighting for?

Answer: To beat Hitler.

Question: What shall we do after the war?

Answer: Doubtless, there will be a lot of problems to be sorted out, but all those problems will be no worse than they are now, and the world minus Hitler will, at any rate, be so much better than the world plus Hitler.

It all seemed so simple, but then, of course, Bobby is obviously right that the war will itself create new problems—that we shall not win the war in that straightforward, simple sense at all—that wars are always won by *tertii gaudentes*—by nations or peoples or philosophies which were not protagonists at all at the beginning of the conflict, but which catch the combatants bathing—or, I suppose we should say, fighting—and then run away with their clothes. Then, after the war, there is that fussy short period during which the people who were progressives before the war think that they are progressives still and do not notice that progress has changed its whole meaning and direction. But before long they get shuffled off and the world settles down to its new direction—if, indeed, it is lucky enough to settle down at all, which this time is by no means certain.

It is surprising how much people talk about progress, and how little they notice that progress, at different times and in different places, means quite different things. At the beginning of the industrial revolution progress meant taking women out of factories; to-day it apparently means putting them back there. When I was up at Oxford, the Liberals were all talking about local option, and being a progressive meant believing in more and more temperance restrictions. Then I went to America, where they had prohibition and were just beginning to be against it, and I found, to my unconcealed delight, that the more I drank the more progressive I was.

Bobby, of course, thinks that we must fight—not because any good will come out of it, but because the moral law must be upheld. He always says that he and the Jesuits are the only people in history who have not believed that the end justifies the means. I do not know if I can follow that. It is very difficult to know what it means in the last analysis. If the future is quite unknowable, then, surely, the pacifist has a strong case, for he can say, "If we can neither tell what will come out of peace nor what will come out of war, then let us have peace, since that is at least immediately the more desirable!" Yet, in a slightly larger sense, I very well see what Bobby means and I understand very well his heartfelt "One good thing has come out of this at any rate: Thank God no one can any longer foresee the future." Up till now, I had always assumed that everything was inevitably moving towards what is known as the Left. It is true that, in some more recent manifestations, the philosophic distinctions between Left and Right were sometimes rather difficult to discern. Still, broadly, I think I was right, and, broadly, that is how they would have gone on moving, if there had not been a war. But now no one can tell. It is not merely the pace of progress that one cannot foretell, but —even more—the direction of it. The question is not: Will the progressives win after the war? Of course they will. That is a question without meaning, because whoever wins will call himself progressive.

> *Treason doth never prosper. What's the reason?*
> *That, if it prosper, none dare call it treason.*

The question is: What will be the direction of progress?

Meanwhile, the sun is shining, and it reminds me of so many days which I have spent bathing or playing tennis or hiking. You know how sensitive I am to weather, and good weather and bad weather alike remind me of other days of the same weather, but, in every other way, so intolerably different from the dreadful present. The sun is an obstinate conservative, and the weather always seems most lovely when the news is most terrible. It was just the same, I remember, when the Germans broke through at Easter, 1918. I read about it, sun-bathing, on a flat stone roof in the intervals of learning the part of Julius Caesar in Shaw's *Caesar and Cleopatra*. I think that it is a certain strengthening consolation to know that the weather at least goes on, though all else crumble. Of course, Ruskin would say that it is pathetic fallacy to imagine that the sun cares about it at all, but I quite agree with Arnold Toynbee that there is much more of the apathetic fallacy than the pathetic fallacy about these days—that is to say, that we make more mistakes by treating human beings as if they were objects than we do by treating objects as if they were human beings. I do not suppose that the sun cares, but it is orthodox enough theology, surely, that God who made the sun cares, and it is Dante's theory that the supreme expression of His love is seen in the sustenance of the natural laws:

L'amor che muove il sol e l'altre stelle.

It is both a consolation and a revelation to think that it is only man that is vile, and that the natural things stand fast. Sorry to harp back to Dante, but terrible happenings do drive one back to the great poets—the only people who say things that, in the last analysis, really mean something.

Love, Peter

2

September 17, 1939.

My dear,

If you want to know why modern plaster walls do not last as long as the old ones, you do not need a husband to tell you that. There's something where even a brother will suffice. The old plaster was full of cowhair, and it was the cowhair that kept it together, but the modern process of taking the hair off the hides has the effect of rotting the hair. Hence, modern plaster cracks in months, where the old plaster used to last for years. Do not use plaster for Mrs. Campbell's walls. You will only have all the walls back on your hands, plus a grievance in a year or two's time, just when there is no labour for repairs.

The idealogue in you will say that here is another example of the superiority of old ways over new. I am not sure. There is bound to be some loss when you do things by mass production. Who but a fool could deny that? But, surely, the answer is that they did things better in the past, when there were fewer of them to do it. But what of it? Who is responsible for the increased population, if not you and your pals who are always going on about a higher birth-rate? You have got it, and now you are hoist with your own petard. No one is more fond than I am of the countryside à la Brueghel's *La Moisson*, but you cannot live off it. It is a terrifying experiment upon which, willy-nilly, we have launched ourselves—this experiment of an urban civilisation of millions and millions of men and women, who must eat daily or die, and who are yet quite divorced from the source of food. Everyone can see today how dangerous it all is, when a bomb may fall on their heads, but I am just as impressed with the danger even in peace, when there are no bombs. Read your Ecclesiasticus. "All these trust in their hands, and every one is wise in his work. Without these cannot a city be inhabited; and they shall not dwell where they will, and go up and down; but they will maintain the state of the world, and all their desire is in the work of their craft." (Good, isn't it? I often wonder if the Bible was nearly as good in the original as it is in English.) Anyway, there is the problem. To say that it is difficult is a truism. To say that we must run away from it, and all live the simple life in the country, is to shirk the whole issue. Civilisation means living *civiliter*, living as citizens, and, unless some people live in cities, you do not get civilisation.

What a bore it is, being able to see both sides of a question! Life is so much easier for those who can't.

Love, Peter

3

My dear,

November's not my month. It is no good pretending that it is. I am a summer man—"a prosperous morning in May" or "the leafy month of June" for me—sun and cricket and bathing and tea in the garden. Yet even the devil among months must have its due, and at six o'clock this morning—when you will be surprised to hear that I was up—I saw the frost on your front lawn shining in the moonlight as if it were snow, and felt it good to be alive. Then came the dawn, as they say in the movies, and that pale, watery, half-apologetic sun of winter picked out the black rooks settled on the ploughland. They start the chorus, and then a thrush joins in and then some wrens. The pigeons coo themselves off the roof of the barn and fly off down into the valley. The clouds are blown across the sky like great battering-rams, and the oaks, which of all the trees alone retain their form of leaves in November, stand like armies to engage them. If only it weren't so cold!

Still, I did not write to tell you only that. I have more progress to report of my stewardship during your absence in Northamptonshire. (Why do people go to Northamptonshire just because there is a war on? What an absurd excuse!) Yesterday—at last—the men came and took down the elm trees—just in time, too, before they fell of their own volition on top of the nursery. Tree-felling by experts is a fascinating business, enjoyed equally by me and the children. The old foreman started by standing with his back to the tree and facing the way that he wished it to fall. He turned round and made a little cut in it with his axe. He made the first attack on the tree with his axe alone. Then, when he had broken ground, the men set to with the saw. The trees were soon down, falling with a lovely, rending crash that set the children all gooey with delight. After that came the loading onto the tractor. There was a revolving drum on the tractor. One man set the chains and hooks on the trunk, and the other moved the tractor forward and backward to his companions' "Whoas," just as if it was a horse, and thus worked the trunk up until it was loaded on to the drag. It was a fascinating sight—fascinating to everybody, apparently, except to two odious little boys who had won scholarships at the secondary school and who rode by on their bicycles with satchels on their backs. They watched for thirty seconds, and then one of them, with pimples on the bridge of his nose and spectacles on the end of it, said to his companion, "There's nothing to see here," and they rode on. I had never before so strongly felt the truth of Bobby's contention that modern education narrows the mind.

I am afraid, now that Advent is coming on, the hens have stopped laying. They are very liturgical birds—your hens. They always stop laying for Advent and usually for Lent—the dirty brutes—lousy scolecobrotes.

Love, Peter

4

December 3, 1939.

My dear,

I commend Robert for his interest in swearing. The older I grow, the more important do I see it that people should use bad language. There is a kind of relaxation of the mind in it, which is the one guarantee against tight-lipped Puritanism. I hate people who are too careful off duty. And, if a boy is going to use bad language, then, indeed, it is but a sign of intelligence that he should study it. By all means, let him write a thesis on it when he comes to take his degree as D. Litt. in the distant future. But he is entirely wrong in imagining that "bloody" is a Victorian modernism, and that there was anything novel in the use of the word when Bernard Shaw used it in *Pygmalion.* Let him turn to Swift's *Journal to Stella* for the 5th of January, 1713, and he will read, "Our frost is broke, but it is bloody cold." That is how clergymen talked to their lady friends in the days of good Queen Anne.

When I was up at Oxford, an undergraduate began a letter to the Bursar: "O thou that sent our Bloody Battels up," which is a genuine line out of *Paradise Regained.* But that is a joke—though, I venture to think, a very good one. Swift is perfectly bona fide.

Does he know the Australian poem in Robert Graves's *Lars Porsena, or the Future of Swearing?* He ought to.

Or that other admirable Australian poem about Tobruk, which begins:

> *The bloody town's a bloody muss,*
> *No bloody trams, no bloody bus,*
> *And no one to care for bloody us—*
> *Oh, bloody, bloody, bloody.*

What a good word it is!

Do not let him ever make the mistake of thinking that anything is new. Everything is much older than the people who say it or use it guess. Have you ever spent New Year's Day at Caerleon? I did once when I was in the motor trade. The children got hold of apples and put gold leaf on them and stuck sprigs of box and the ends of hazel-nuts into them. Then they put them onto tripod sticks and carried them round the town, and people gave them sweets. Why did they do this? Caerleon means the "Fort of the Legion." The Second Augustan Legion was stationed there, and Martial tells us that it was a Roman custom to do this at New Year's time, for it brought "good crops and wealth in the New Year." The Legion left Caerleon in about 400 A.D., and, jumping over King Arthur like a hopped draughtsman, the children of Caerleon have continued to do this ever since. So there.

Love, Peter

5

My dear,

What can I say? Of course, I will do what little I can do to help with the bringing up of the boys. You cannot imagine how flattered I am. Could I have ever imagined that anyone would have invited me to have an influence over their children? I had always thought that I was the Wicked Uncle against whom children had to be warned. It is not you who have to thank me; it is I who have to thank you—and for a deeper reason, too, than that of mere thanks for flattery.

You remember Dr. Johnson, who hated people who gushed out with their verbal condolences. "They pay you by sympathising," he said. So often, particularly in these days, that is what the conventions of society compel us to do. We have to write and say how sorry we are that someone has been killed. We are sorry in a sort of way. It would be boorish not to say so, and still more boorish to introduce our qualifications into our letters of condolence. And yet we aren't, in ninety-nine cases out of a hundred, really so very sorry as all that. It does not mean that we have less for dinner that night, or enjoy it less. Sometimes we,

> *Not being really bad at heart*
> *Remember Johnny with a start,*

but rarely, I am afraid, and, in these days, when there are so many Johnnys, all the more rarely.

And then someone goes that you really do mind—not in that vague, negative way that you wished him no harm and wished his relatives no harm, which is what minding is apt to mean in general, but mind right down in the bottom of your bones. And how can one show it? Just piling on the epithets a bit does not show it. Rather the reverse. The more epithets, the more the impression of insincerity. One can only prove sincerity by doing something. And is there anything that one can do? Nothing is more demoralising than to be anxious to do something and have nothing to do—to be all dressed up spiritually and have no place to go and that is why, my dear, I am enormously grateful to you, when you tell me that there is something I can do. It is I who have to be grateful to you—not you to me.

Compassion, suffering with, the desire to suffer with—it is the nemesis of all things, the refutation of all extreme hedonism and of all extreme individualism. You know how conventional conversations go:

"I was so sorry to hear your news. Is there anything that I can do to help?"

"It is so kind of you. I don't know that there really is."

"Well, you will promise to let me know if I can do anything, won't you? I should like to be able to do something."

"Of course, I will. Thank you so much. It is most awfully kind of you."

And neither of them ever gives the matter a thought again. And then, twice, it may be, in a lifetime one uses these familiar conventional phrases and really means them —wants to help, not in the vague sense of being willing to help, but in the positive sense of being passionate to help, as if all purpose will have gone out of life if one is not allowed to help. Twice, it may be, in a lifetime one uses language like that, really meaning it, and once, probably, the other fellow never guesses that you mean it and just answers according to the conventions—and that's that. And once, perhaps, in a lifetime, if you're lucky, it comes off.

One of the greatest triumphs in all literature was, surely, Pompilia's at the end of *The Ring and the Book*— even though it was a posthumous triumph. You remember? Her one desire had been to help Guido, and Guido had hurt her, betrayed her, robbed her, finally murdered her—had given back no return in love at all, not even a return of suffering, not even a return of decency. And then, at the last, in his moment of condemnation, he breaks down, as it were, into humanity.

> *Abate, Cardinal, Christ, Maria, God,*
> *Pompilia, will you let them murder me?*

He turns to her at the last, and the curtain goes superbly down on that. The old Pope, you remember, had prayed that *"Guido see one instant and be saved."*
It would all make a very good play—if plays were good.
God bless you, my dear,

Peter

6

August 15, 1940.

Ruth dear,

Spiritual consolations? And from me? What's George for? You see, before one dare even to venture to offer consolation, one must, first, believe with absolute assurance that it is all true, and, second, have the objective title-deeds to prove one's sincerity. Now, quite frankly, I am not yet quite sure. Sometimes I think that it's true, and sometimes I think that it's less than the truth, and sometimes that it's more than the truth, and sometimes, like Browning at High Mass, "This is too good to be true." But I can't say that I know, and, until one knows, one had better not talk.

> *But ask not bodies doomed to die*
> *To what abode they go,*
> *Since knowledge is but sorrow's spy,*
> *It is not safe to know.*

And then there is the question of title-deeds. Of course, I know as well as Dr. Johnson that one can have good principles and bad practice, and that no man can well judge what is the degree of virtue in another. That is a principle which I might well invoke in mitigation in the dock, but I can hardly invoke it in the pulpit. Before preaching, one ought not only to be virtuous, but to appear so. If you can't manage that, then it is probably best to keep your spiritual life a very private life.

The Christian religion, whether it be a true religion or a false religion, is, at any rate, a very wonderful religion. It has a good many advantages over any other religion that has ever been invented, and one of them is this: Take all the other religions and philosophies that are worth serious consideration—Judaism, Hellenism, Stoicism, Platonism, or, to come on to modern post-Christianities, Shelleyanism, Kantianism, pantheism, Marxianism, God knows what-ism. The essence of them —one and all—is that they are a bit inhuman, and none of them more so than humanitarianism. They attempt to solve the problem of sorrow by cheating—by denying it. "The One (or the Absolute or the Will of God) is. What is, is, and all that you have got to do is to accept it. If a baby died, then it was the will of God that that baby should die—and, if that was not your will, that just shows what a stinking sort of fellow you were. If humanity gets in the way of your seeing that, then empty yourself of your humanity as fast as you can."

So the pre-Christian world and the post-Christian world alike have tended to fall into two classes—the people who did not try to make sense of things and thought it the best plan just to gather rosebuds while they might— and those who, in order that things might make sense, were ready to make them inhuman. But the point about Christ is that He did say that things make sense, but He also did say that sorrow was both real and also proper. I remember that at Summer Fields we used to have a thing called Bible-reading every morning for half an hour. Everybody had to get up in turn and read a verse of the Bible, and, at the end, I suppose, the master jawed a bit about what had been read—I forget about that. Anyway, one day a boy got up and read the two words: "Jesus wept"—they form a verse all by themselves, you know— and then sat down again. It seemed so ridiculous that we all burst out laughing, and then, of course, there was a hell of a row, and we were all told off for irreverence. But, as the result of it all, I remember that verse very well, and a very important verse it is. "Jesus wept." There is no verse which tells us that "Aristotle wept" or "Marcus Aurelius wept" or "Immanuel Kant wept."

Don't you see, my dear, that this verse and, indeed, the whole Christian doctrine of sorrow should be an enormous consolation to you at such a time as this? Man, the great philosopher, may say that it is an unholy thing to be unmanly. But God is not ashamed to be unmanly. God does not deny sorrow or bid you deny sorrow. He only bids you compare your sorrow with His own. *"O vos, qui transitis per viam, attendite et videte si est dolor sicut dolor meus."*

"That's all very well," you say, "but how do you reconcile the reality of sorrow with the claim that the scheme of creation is a good scheme of a good God?" Well, how did Cleopatra reconcile it, who, after all, knew a thing or two, even if she was not exactly a regularly recognised doctor of the Church?

> *The stroke of death is as a lover's pinch*
> *Which hurts and is desired.*

43

And that was what mattered.

> *Sir, you and I must part, but that's not it,*
> *Sir, you and I have loved, but there's not it.*

What mattered was to live life on a plane of intensity, where the language of hedonism was an irrelevance, on a plane where sorrow was, indeed, an intense reality, but where, at the same time, it was a kind of joy, because it was suffered for somebody else. Of course, I know that that does not quite answer the argument, if you care to press it. You can say: "Perhaps a good God did make the world like that, but why did He make it like that if He was perfectly good? The Fall? But who made Adam? Who made the devil? Who made the apple?" And, of course, there is no answer to such questions, except to say, "Ask George." After all, he's paid for answering. But I suspect that the real answer was given by Dean Church, when he said, "Christ did not come to clear up the perplexity, but to show us which side to take"—to teach that we may weep when there are tears for things and not be ashamed of doing so.

You see, you've won. I have preached a sermon, after all—and, what's more, a damned good one.

Yours, Peter

7

October 7, 1940.

My dear Ruth,

Of all forms of insanity, scientific education in schools is, by far, the most dangerous. It is sometimes said that it is desirable that scientists should know some science. I cannot, myself, see the necessity. The man who made the bomb which fell in the next street last week doubtless knew a lot of science— and so did the man who made the A-A gun which shot the plane down—and the surgeon who patched together the German pilot's face with little bits of skin off his bottom—and the new German bomber who blew both surgeon and pilot to pieces last night, just as the operation was finished. They all knew a lot of science, and it would have been very much better, as far as I can see, for everybody, if only they had known a little less, and we all might then have remained in the comparatively civilised conditions of the Dark Ages.

But I am not concerned to argue that scientists should not know science, but rather to ask what sort of people ought to be allowed to be scientists. Science is in itself neutral, neither good nor bad, but he who is master of it to-day is master of a power potent for incalculable destruction. It is immensely dangerous that that power should fall into the hands of those who cannot understand what it is that they may destroy. By all means—if I may speak seriously—let us have technical and vocational training of every sort—the very best that we can get—but do not, on pain of death, allow anyone to touch it who has not first had a good general religious and literary education to teach him what civilisation is about.

I cannot think of anything that modern history has more terrifyingly demonstrated than the absolute, literal truth of

> *The man that hath no music in himself,*
> *Nor is not mov'd with concord of sweet sounds,*
> *Is fit for treasons, stratagems, and spoils;*
> *The motions of his spirit are dull as night,*
> *And his affections dark as Erebus:*
> *Let no such man be trusted.*

All tone-deaf people should, in my opinion, be disfranchised.

I have nothing against prose, but I think that the world could, if it had to, get on without its prose. Poetry is what matters—I mean the great dozen or so central poets of the world's story. A boy who knows what they said knows about all that there is any need to know, and a boy who does not know them knows nothing.

"Ah, if there shall ever arise," asks the Caliph, "a nation whose people have forgotten poetry, or whose poets have forgotten the people, though they send their ships round Taprobane and their armies across the hills of Hindustan, though their city be greater than Babylon of old, though they mine a league into earth or mount to the stars on wings—what of them?"

"They will be a dark patch on the world," says Hassan.

This may, perhaps, sound like exaggeration and paradox, but I cannot honestly see how anyone can deny it. The world used to be run by people who knew that they were what they were because they had inherited from past generations, who knew the creeds and the codes on which their society was built, and whence those creeds and codes were derived. They were often very bad men and quite unworthy of the privileges which they had inherited. They sometimes cynically exploited their privileges. Yet, in those days society did at least go on. In this world, in which it is bliss to be alive at dawn, and almost a miracle if you survive until after luncheon, society is manifestly coming to an end as quickly as it possibly can.

I am no great one for hereditary privilege. I am quite partial to the argument that the dustman's son should have as full educational opportunities as the duke's son, but what educational reform has come to mean in the modern world is simply that neither of them shall be educated at all. When I was at Eton during the last war, Alec Waugh's *Loom of Youth* came out, and everybody started ranting against classical education. The argument then was that learning Greek and Latin was a waste of time, and I should be much more profitably employed on commercial geography. But to-day the argument is that it is a great privilege to know Greek, but why should the rich be privileged? If everybody cannot learn Greek, nobody shall.

So, apparently, no one is to be educated at all. That

seems to me the true drift of modern educational reform. I have been amazed, in my experience at the War Office, at the low level of education, whether among officers or among typists. It is rare indeed to know the meaning of quite ordinary English words. A girl who knows the elements of grammar or of punctuation, who can spell, who knows the A.B.C. of geography is almost a freak. Whether women should be educated is debatable. That they are not is a certainty.

So, if Martin does not want to do classics, that is a pity, but it would be folly to allow his wish to be a deciding factor. The thing to look at with children in their teens is not their passing preferences—which are a mere accident of the rate of maturity—but their parents' tastes. Children are as their parents, and, if the parents have literary tastes, you can be pretty sure that the children will have them, too, in good time. In such a time as this it would be a crime to deny a literary education to one who, we may guess from his parents, will one day probably come to literary taste. Of course, he does not like Virgil now; who ever heard of any one under forty liking Virgil? Who ever heard of anyone over forty who was not very grateful that he had been made to learn Virgil twenty-five years before?

Yours ever, Peter

P.S. History specialisation is another story. The real answer to it is not that it is not the way to learn history. It is just a soft option for boys who cannot or do not want to learn anything. A boy must first learn what men are—

48

and that he can only learn from literature. It is futile to start passing judgments on the little corner of man's activities that have to do with politics and economics, until he has first learnt what man is.

> *How small of all that human hearts endure*
> *That part which kings or laws can cause or cure.*

The part has, it is true, considerably increased since Johnson's time, but no one knows better than you that there are what Newman used to call "the privileges of the heart," which no totalitarian dictator can invade, however much he may wish it—and that it is they that really matter.

8

November 17, 1940.

My dear,

Of course, the answer is to do nothing. There is a lot to be said against boarding schools, but these have, at least, this advantage—that parents can keep out of these rows. Keep out of them. I have never, myself, understood why schoolmasters make such a fuss about smoking, but there it is—and boys smoke, not particularly because they like cigarettes, but because they want to prove to the world that they are bold and bad and brave and grown-up. All that is very tiresome and very natural—as tiresome as mumps and as natural as mumps. A boy who did not go through a certain phase of "fourteenitis" might be a convenience, but he would be an oddity.

So there is nothing to worry about. What with the experiences that he has gone through and the experiences that the world is going through and the natural experiences of his years, nothing is less surprising than that Martin should have his "phase." It is the schoolmasters' job to cope with it. That is what they are paid for. Make them do it. It is important that they should do it, because they are only concerned with Martin here and now and for a few years. They can be rigid and red-tapy in a way that would be very dangerous for you, his mother. That is what he needs—someone who says quite fairly, but a little woodenly: "I don't know anything about that. This is the rule, and you broke it—and this is the penalty"—so as to convince him that he is not a special case, whereas to you, of course, he must always be a special case.

Make his housemaster tell you quite frankly all that they have against him and what he has done and what they have done, so that you know what is going on, but don't say anything to Martin about it. Don't let on to him that you know. Some boys like talking about their rows, and some boys are humiliated and shy about them. There is nothing for it but to accept each boy as he is. If he wants to talk about himself, well and good. But, if he does not, respect his privilege of reticence. Don't ask him about it, and, above all, don't try and worm it out of him by hints and leading questions and other such devices that are most truly of the devil.

All this I would say of any boy at any time. Obviously, it is doubly important to keep an eye on boys at a time of the breaking of the nations such as this. You know what a World War can do with a schoolboy. The last World War produced me. There is no saying what this World War may produce. But keep an extra eye open, just in case the growing pains should turn out to be something more than growing pains. But there again and even more so—mum's the word. Nothing is more calculated to make a boy odd than the knowledge that he is constantly being watched to see if he is odd. What a bloody fool that headmaster is, with all his rubbish about psychoanalysis! Just the worst thing possible for boys.

Yours, Peter

9

November 30, 1940.

My dearest,

Thank you so much for your letter, but what can I say to you about Marjorie? I can answer the ordinary letters of condolence. I write off the conventional phrases, like somebody writing in his sleep. I do not care very much what I write, and I know very well that they will not care very much what they read, and, yet, it is kind of them all to write, and kindness is a great deal. But what can I write to you? You see, I remember so well all that I wrote to you about compassion and about the will to do something and the need to do something, not so very many months ago. It puts me in a terrible, funny difficulty. With you I am terrified, not of asking too much, but of asking too little. After all that I had written, after the enormous compliment that you had paid me of asking me to help you to bring up your children, it would seem churlish indeed to reply: "Thank you very much. I can't just think of anything at the moment. I will let you know if anything turns up." It would seem as if I was hardening in the very nastiest sort of way—sinking back from that acceptance of the human which I had preached as one of the main lessons of Christianity. "Nothing is here for tears," writes Laurence Binyon. How little he knew!

Yes, my dear, you are a person to whom it is just a

waste of time to lie. It is no good inventing something that I pretend to want merely to be able to ask you something —no good just saying, "I should be most awfully grateful if you could come up to London every other Thursday and bring me a bottle of smelling-salts," or words to that effect. And the blank truth is that there is no definite, concrete service that I can ask of you similar to that which you asked of me. The nature of things forbids a parallel. An uncle can be a father, but an aunt cannot be a mother —and that, however bad the uncle, however good the aunt. The intimacy of the mother's relationship is such that it can never be substituted. The motherless just have to go without. It would be a lie in the soul to pretend otherwise. I am sure that you understand.

But there is something that a sister can do. You know how this leaves a man longing for feminine sympathy and company and yet, for the moment at any rate, hating, loathing, recoiling from any sort of companionship which carries with it any sort of tiny, little image of a kind that has in it any comparison or rivalry with the companion- ship that is lost; and it is at such a time, my dear, that one turns to the only sort of feminine friendship that can, in no sort of way, be a disloyalty, to the friendship of the best and the wisest and the bravest of sisters. "*Soror unica*," says Catullus. May I?

Peter

10

My dear Ruth,

I do not know what reports, if any, Martin may have
sent back about my week-end at Trumpinghurst, but I
enjoyed my time no end—and, especially, the match on
Saturday afternoon. Martin really is going to be a good
cricketer—an absolutely lovely schoolboy bat—I've never
seen anyone of his age with a better off-drive, and he seems
to me to be less bothered with nerves than Bobby used to
be. That must be your doing. Though he did not make
the most runs, he was far and away the best player on the
field.

I know you do not think that cricket matters—that
is was half a fad and half a joke of Bobby's and mine to
pretend that it matters. Women do think that, but I don't
agree. I think that it matters a lot—for better or worse.

The next best player was a young Greek, called
Eleutheros Corizis. He was light-haired and tall and blue-
eyed, and he looked more like a Norwegian than a Levan-
tine. But I suppose, for that matter, so did Hermes. He and
Martin made quite a nice little stand for the third wicket.
On Sunday Martin brought him to tea. He was quite an
amusing cove for a schoolboy—the son of a Greek Communist who lived in Liverpool—very rich, and made a lot
of money out of selling carpets, and sent it all back to fin-

ance Greek Communists in their struggle against foreign capital. The boy was talking about his preparatory school. His father had sent him to some crank preparatory school, where upper-class Bolshevists paid through the nose, and where no one was allowed to interfere with any of the boys' impulses, for fear of setting up complexes. "So I hid under a sofa one day. A parent was sitting on the sofa talking to the headmaster, so I bit him in the calf of his leg," said Eleutheros. The headmaster said that he could not interfere, because, if you rebuke boys, it created an inhibition, but the parent turned out to be a Labour peer. So there was a fearful row, and the school had to close down.

This is what he told me—all doubtless untrue, and he was obviously a little too pleased with himself for being so rum, and thought it smart to make jokes about his father, who, for all I know, may not even have been mad at all. Some parents aren't. I asked old Parsons what he thought of Master Corizis, and he found him rather a handful. "Not what one would call, to use a technical term, exactly a good boy," he said. It reminded me of Samuel Butler's descriptions of Mr. Gladstone as "a good man, in the worst possible sense of the word." I told him so. "Well," he said, "the headmaster's always taking foreign boys to prove that he's broad-minded, and then expelling them to prove that he's pure-minded. It really is rather a nuisance."

"He's a good cricketer, at any rate," I said. "That was a lovely boundary he hit with his cut past third-man yesterday."

"Ah, yes," said Parsons with a sigh, "but then should foreigners hit boundaries?"

I rather like Parsons, I must say. I do tend to like schoolmasters on the whole—if only out of reaction against their critics. If a man makes rocking-horses or aeroplanes, or extracts appendixes, no one pretends to know how to do the job except the small company of his co-professionals. But every mortal man and woman has spent ten dreary years sitting on a bench, gaping up at a pedagogue and wondering how he does it. The result is that everyone thinks that he could teach just as well as a schoolmaster if only he wanted to, and everyone is ready to lay down the law about it. "Really," old Booker used to say at Eton, "parents are the last people who ought to be allowed to have children."

Martin seems to be doing all right, as far as I could make out. Naturally, it all depends on what one means by "all right." I was never, myself, a one for offensive virtue. Boys ought to strike a happy medium, "neither too good nor too bad," like the judge who avoided partiality on the one hand and impartiality on the other. Martin seems to do that all right.

Yours, Peter

11

My dear Ruth,

If you really want to know why cricket is important,
I will gladly tell you. First, it obviously is important in
a schoolboy, because it at once makes him prominent
above his schoolfellows. There is good and bad, danger
and opportunity in that. It at once makes him an aristocrat
among schoolboys, subject to all an aristocrat's temptations and all his opportunities. It may give him just the
right amount of self-confidence, or it may make him
altogether insolent and intolerable. That depends on the
individual. I am not saying that being good at games is
necessarily a good thing. I am merely saying that it makes
a difference—just as being a duke makes a difference.

But there is this, further, to be said for games. The
older I become, the more I come to think games important for exactly the same reason as that for which m' tutor
at Eton used to think them unimportant. He used to say,
"That's all you think about now, but, when you grow up
and get out into the world, you will find people bothering about things that really matter." Well, when I did
grow up, I found that the things that really mattered were
the destiny of man and the poetry of Dante and the dozen
or so other people since the beginning of time who have
really understood what's what—in fact, what King Lear

called "the mystery of things"—but I did not find, as m'
tutor had led me to believe, that these problems were in
normal occupation of the mind of every grown-up person. Much to the contrary. They thought of such things
much less than we had thought of them at school, and, in
so far as they thought about anything that even pretended
to be serious, they thought about politics and money-
making. Now cricket seems to some much less dangerous
than either politics or money-making. There are a lot of
people who really do think that their happiness is in
direct proportion to their income, and it is not so. There
are a lot of people who really do think that the whole fate
of a nation depends on the result of a general election, who
make no allowance for the smallness of the difference in
practise between rival parties, the little that a government
or a minister can do to change the trend of things, the trivi-
ality of so much of it *sub specie aeternitatis*.

Now, the great advantage that cricket has over politics is that it never pretends to be more than itself. No one
imagines that the destiny of an immortal soul depends on
the holding of a catch—that a generation will be made
happy or miserable by the result of an afternoon's game.
The game is ephemeral, beautiful, lovable. As such, it is
neither more nor less than are all the purely secular activities of man.

> *All beauteous things for which we live*
> *By laws of time and space decay,*
> *But, oh, the very reason why*
> *We clasp them is because they die.*

But cricket, and bathing, and the first crocuses, and the wind on the hill-side, and the sun shining on a sailboat a little way out to sea, and apple trees in September—they are all superior to other secular things, because they never pretend to be more than they are. They are, they are enjoyed; they are remembered. Who but God can ask for more?

> *For beauty vanishes—beauty passes*
> *However rare—rare it be,*
> *And, when I crumble, who will remember*
> *The lady of the West Countree?*

And so am I glad that both Martin and Robert can play cricket. Like Sir Richard Grenville, I would have done my duty as a man is bound to do even had their bats been the crookedest in Christendom. But it would have been a fight against scepticism. Is there any real sense in educating people who cannot bat?

Yours, Peter

12

August 5, 1941.

My dear Ruth,

I had rather an interesting evening with your Martin,
as he was passing through London, and got him to talk
quite a lot. He was particularly bothered about a dream
that he said he had been having, and he asked what I could
make of it. He said that he often used to dream about
Bobby. That was natural enough, though he hated it,
because he so minded the waking up and the discovery
that Bobby was not alive after all. But there was one particular dream that he had several times, in which Bobby
was walking along a road that ran up a very steep hill. At
the end of the road could be seen the hill-top, crowned by
a building—perhaps a small church, perhaps an old fort or
the ruins of it. There were houses on either side of this
street—many of them in ruins. He had never seen so many
ruins in a single street—not even in blitzed London. Just
ahead of the place which Bobby had reached, some barbed
wire was stretched across the road on posts. To his immediate left there was a gap in the houses, and some stone
steps ran up to a garden gate in a little stone wall. Martin
said that he knew, as one does in dreams, that there was a
great danger to Bobby lurking behind that wall, yet he
was impotent to do anything about it. Then Bobby turned
and looked up the steps, and, as he did so, a shot rang out

from the top of them, and he fell down dead. Then the grinning face of young Corizis appeared over the wall, and, with its appearance, the dream faded.

"Did your father ever know Tony Corizis?" I asked.

"Of course not," said Martin.

"What's happened to him now?" I asked.

"Oh, he just got his eleven at the end of last term," said Martin. "He is not really a very good bat. He has some nice strokes, but he has got no patience, and he is apt to lose his temper when he gets out—which is boring."

What could I say about all this? Could I interpret the king's dream as Joseph did? Dreams seem to me like jig-saw puzzles that nobody has arranged. All the little pieces out of the past come trotting into the dream for no rhyme or reason. Sometimes one goes on thinking about the thing that one has been thinking about during the day—and that makes sense—but, at other times, there pops up into one's dream someone whom one had known casually a quarter of a century before and had never thought of since—God knows why. Who is it who settles what pieces of the puzzle to put into the kitty?

"Yes," said Martin, "if you like, that accounts for the people. But the scene? I had never seen that road in my life."

"One sees all sorts of things in dreams that one has not seen in life," I said.

I think J. W. Dunne's probably right, don't you? I don't mean in his whole theory of Observer No. 1 and Observer No. 2. That all seems to me abominably compli-cated, and there is a lot in it that I can't understand. But in the general dream-time theory? Suppose that time is not ultimate, as all philosophers except Bergson agree. Then all experience must, as it were, exist in a book that is already all printed. Normally, we read through this book line by line, but under certain exceptional circumstances some of us—those with second sight and the rest—can jump ahead or jump back a few lines. It cannot be a very common or a very reliable gift, this second sight—the fortunes of book-makers prove that—but I have no doubt that it exists. Well, I think that it is probably true that, in dreams, some strange master of ceremonies, on a plan that is apparently entirely arbitrary, takes shots impartially from the past and shots from the future and mixes them together into a dream.

"Well," said Martin, "what can I expect to happen?"

"Oh, you can't expect anything to happen like that," I said. "Dreams do not come true in that sense. I am prepared to believe that every particular that you see in a dream either was or will be a part of your experience. But they are all jumbled up quite differently. You cannot make anything out of them. How can this dream be going to come true, when your father is dead already?"

I tell you all this, well, because I do tell you things. I have no reason to think that Martin was really worried about it—had dreams-on-the-brain—and I daresay that he has forgotten all about it by now. But I am glad, I must say, that he spilled the tale out to me rather than to that fool of a headmaster. The headmaster would have jumped for joy and had him psychoanalysed before you could say "Jack Robinson." The old fool! I have nothing against psychoanalysis—which is a long, bogus Greek name for odd people being treated kindly and sympathetically. Wise schoolmasters ought to watch boys carefully—particularly in such times as these—but they should not always show that they are watching them. Normal boys should seem to be treated in a fairly offhand, rule-of-thumb way. That headmaster always gives me the impression that he is as much ashamed of a boy who is not suffering from an Oedipus-complex as a snob would be of a boy who dropped his h's. When I go down there, I always expect to find some wretched boy, standing in disgrace in a corner, with a notice pinned round his neck, "I Do Not Have Erotic Dreams About My Grandmother."

Yours, Peter

13

December 17, 1941.

My dear,

Boys leaving school do lie. Whether it be a good thing or a bad thing, there it is. I remember ever so well my last Sunday at Eton, walking arm in arm with David coming back from the last private business meeting of Pop. David said to me, "Well, Peter, what do you feel like about leaving?"

I answered, "I suppose one ought to be feeling the 'dear Mother Eton, far from thee, happiest days of your life' feeling, but I'm afraid I just can't. I'm afraid that I just feel that it's all rather a bore and high time I moved on to something else."

"So do I," said David. "I just can't feel anything else. I thought I should mind no end, but, now it comes to it, I don't mind a bit."

I went off to Oxford, and David went off to South America, and we never saw each other again for sixteen years, but, when we did meet, we dined at the club, and we both agreed that, in real truth, we had minded like hell, minded as we never minded anything before or since, and that not only did we often think that our schooldays were the happiest days of life, but that it had damned well proved to be so. It is ignorance of the world to come that makes the end of schooldays such a terrific wrench, so blank a catastrophe.

> *But whether, stepping forth, my soul shall see*
> *New prospects or fall sheer, a blinded thing,*
> *There is, O death, thy hourly victory,*
> *And there, O grave, thy sting.*

And, if he guessed how great a fraud life would be, I doubt if anyone would ever have the courage to leave school at all. Let us hope that death will prove better. David confessed to me that after our talk he went off to his tutor's and shut himself up in his room and wept like a pig, and I went down alone to Windsor Bridge and leaned over it for half an hour, looking at the river rippling by.

You see, boys don't know what other boys are like. I thought this sentimentality was a private weakness of my own. So did David. So did all the rest of us. We were all emperors, and we all had no clothes on, but we none of us guessed it of one another. You must remember all that, when you think of Martin to-day. You cannot quite understand—no woman can quite understand—what leaving a public school means to a boy, particularly to a boy who has been good at games, has bestridden that little world like a colossus, and is now going out to he knows not what. You cannot understand, and he cannot tell you, because he does not understand, himself, and, therefore, being inarticulate, takes refuge in shyness, or even in an affectation of hardness that could impose on no one; and Martin, perhaps, has taken onto himself an extra coating of shyness simply because he has a certain sensibility greater than that of the other boys at Trumpinghurst, who are, as far as I can gather, a somewhat philistine lot.

For all his former complaints about the classics, they are beginning to get a hold on him. He is no scholar. He is no great dab, it seems, at grammar and composition, but he is quite genuinely captured by great poetry. They catered for that sort of chap at Eton. It was one of the advantages of our arrogance that we liked people who liked things, even when the things were not such as could be turned to any pot-hunting benefit. But these more competitive, smaller schools, when they are not teaching science, seem determined to teach everything else as if it was a branch of science.

> *And, as my father used to say*
> *In eighteen-sixty-three,*
> *When once you start*
> *On all this art*
> *Good-bye moralitee*

seems to be their motto. To enjoy a lesson seems to have about it a smack of indecency. I remember, one day in Martin's room, there was a chap called Philsby, or some such name. Martin was reading Propertius, and he said that *"Sunt apud infernos tot milia formosarum,"* was a lovely line.

"Oh, for God's sake," said Philsby, "I mean to say, for God's sake."

So you have got to allow for all that. Of course, he hates leaving, but equally, of course, he would die sooner than confess as much. But, what he does not guess is that Philsby hates it, too, and that Philsby, for all I know, in his most secret heart of hearts is mad-cracky about Propertius. In sixteen years they will meet together and dine at the club and it will all come out. But in the meantime, you and I—and particularly you—know all these things, understand them, allow for them, but let not wild horses nor the slings and arrows of outrageous fortune persuade you to refer to them, unless and until Martin asks you to do so. There are the privileges of the heart, and all companionship between the generations is intolerable, if these privileges are not respected. But need I tell any mother this?

And need I, alas, tell a mother this further truth? All that I have said so far would apply to any boy at any date. But at such a time as this there are further simmerings, peculiar to the time, in such a brain as Martin's. I can understand them very well, for I, too, you remember, left school in the middle of a European war. In normal times young men think of themselves as, for all intents and purposes, immortal; death is so enormously distant that it does not enter into their calculations as a present reality. But, when some of those who left last year or the year before are already dead, when the war shows no sign of ending, it is not possible to be so neglectfully defiant. One must at least wonder, and some people prefer thus to live life in an expectation of death. That makes a difference. The difference, indeed, varies from boy to boy. It makes, perhaps, one a saint and another a profligate; one too serious and another too reckless. What effect it will have on Martin I do not yet prophesy; I only say that you must remember that he is living under this strange strain and allow for it.

"Is it likely that I would not remember it?" you ask, and I stand rebuked.

Sorry, my dear, for being such a fool.

Yours ever, Peter

14

February 17, 1942.

My dear Ruth,

Considering all the trouble that he takes about it, I do not think that Bernard Shaw has such a very good brain. I mean, supposing that we all became vegetarians and non-smokers, and wore knickerbockers and went for bicycle rides, could not we have good brains, too? At least, we could have as good brains as Bernard Shaw, because, although he is a witty, kindly fellow, his fundamental philosophy is about the silliest that any human being ever had. I should have thought that a brain was the one thing that he had not got. Yet, if Martin is going through a phase of Shavianism, I should not be very seriously worried about it. Shaw, as people go these days, is comparatively conservative. What is he likely to teach him? To believe in the Life-Force, which means absolutely nothing—to believe in Socialism—which in these days means even less—to stop smoking, which might do him no great harm, if only there was the least chance that he would do it. Shaw's follies, after all, are all above the board, and I do not know that any great harm will come of them, so long as Martin grows out of them before he is ninety, as I am sure that he will.

Yours, Peter

68

15

My dear,

My really sincere opinion is that there is a great deal
to be said for ostriches—within reason. I know nothing at
all, for good or bad, about the goings-on of Martin's
private life. (If I did know something and was keeping it
from you, I should be guilty of a great breach of faith.)
Once, when I went to see him at Oxford, he got tight, but
that, if a vice, is certainly not a secret one, and "intoxica-
tion," as Boswell so truly remarked, "is a thing that might
happen to a man at any time."

I am concerned solely with generalisation.

My generalisation is this: I quite agree with Keats:
"The imagination of a boy is healthy, and the mature
imagination of a man is healthy; but there is a space of life
between in which the soul is in a ferment, the character
undecided, the way of life uncertain, the ambitions thick-
sighted; thence proceed mawkishness and all the thousand
bitters."

Very few people—very few boys, at any rate—are so
well-balanced that they can make the transition from boy-
hood to manhood without doing a number of foolish
things in between. Young men of twenty are bloody fools,
and Oxford is the place to which they are sent to be
bloody fools in.

So—I am arguing, of course, entirely from general probability and on no knowledge of the particular facts. I daresay that Martin has done some foolish things, but, even if so and even if I knew of them, I should not be seriously worried about them. What matters in a young man is not his conduct, but his parents. A young man of twenty may be doing anything, but you can be quite certain that by thirty he will be doing the same sort of things that the parents did. If his parents were good, he will turn out good, and, if his parents were rotters, he will turn out a rotter. So I have not many fears about Martin. I think that I am more likely to form an essentially right judgment on him if I do not know all the petty details of his present life and those of his undergraduate friends.

"That," you may say, "is all very well, but it is a barefaced evasion of the responsibility that you promised to undertake for me. You promised me that you would look after Martin for me, and, now, all that you are doing is to give excuses why he need not be looked after." I sympathise with you. There is, of course, the hundredth case where the laws of heredity do not work. I have never met such a case myself. I have never heard of a boy who went to the bad when his parents were good. Of course, the parents sometimes appeared good, or thought them-selves good—but that is entirely a different point. I have never heard of real virtue in a parent that did not receive reward in the son. Yet, the varieties of human nature are infinite. I cannot absolutely deny the possibility, and you naturally want reassurance. And, again, you want reassur-ance that his habits, transient as they may be, are not such as would some day land you and him in a blaze of inconvenient publicity. You would prefer, for instance, that, if it can be avoided, he should not murder a policeman.

I am willing to do my best to reassure you and to take all the trouble that I can to obtain the reassurance. I only want you, in all seriousness, my dear, to understand the rules of the game. What can I do? I can, of course, ask his dons how he is getting on. I do that for what it is worth. It is not worth much. Then I can see him from time to time and talk to him and get to know him. I flatter myself that I have done a good deal of this and done it fairly well, and that we are as good friends as it is proper to be with the gap of age between us. But we are of different generations, and there is an iron law of decency to be preserved, if friendship is to leap across that gap and to survive. He, the younger, might possibly confide in me, but I, the older, must never try to force his confidence. I must not question him directly. Still less must I try and worm confidences out of him. If I did so, I should doubly damn myself in his eyes. First, he would be embarrassed at having to confess, or, as the case might be, to lie. Second, he would rightly suspect my motives—suspect that mixed in among them was the prurience of a dirty old man.

So I ask no questions and I hear no lies, but, at the same time, I can learn a great deal. But what I am learning to know—I must always remind myself and remind you—is the essential Martin, and not the accidental Martin. I know his views on religion, his views on poetry, his feeling for mystery, his ataraxia, his love of the wind, the longing

71

for home—a thousand things that make me like him very much—and I assure you with all confidence and with all sincerity that you, my dear, are lucky in your son, as you were lucky in your husband, and no one could say more than that.

But for the accidents I will not answer—for what he may or may not have done upon some occasion. I repeat that I have no shade of evidence or gossip on the matter. I am arguing simply on general principle. Some dozen years ago I got to know very well indeed, as I thought, a young man whom I will not name, as his name would be know to you. I was about thirty then and he about twenty-two. I would have sworn that he was extremely high-principled, religious and, indeed, puritanical. I was, if anything, somewhat ashamed of my own laxities in his presence. Then, quite by chance, I discovered that during all the period of our friendship his life had been extremely irregular and immoral. But the interesting thing about my judgment was that, though I was bang wrong about the accidents, I was bang right about the essence. He did soon afterwards marry a wife and proved himself a model husband. He was one of that rare type of employer who really accepts the welfare of his work-people as a religious vocation. And, when the war came, he went out to it and got killed, in a peculiarly gallant manner, in an effort to rescue a comrade from certain death.

Of course, I am your most humble and obedient servant. If you want me to set my spies on, to submit Martin to a third degree to elicit every detail of his misspent youth, I jump to obey. But I do not think that you wish me to do this. The only way to treat the young, as I think you know better than I, is to trust them—to trust them sometimes even, as it were, against their temporary, accidental selves. I know this from my own experience—because I am—because "my name is Lazarus and I live."

God bless you, my dear. What a good mother you are and what a good sister!

Love, Peter

16

March 1, 1912.

My dear,

It is all a matter of apples. I have just thought of this in my bath, and it seems to me to be most frightfully true. All history is the history of four apples. First, there was the apple of Eve from which all trouble comes—in a general way. Then, there was the apple of Paris, whence the "demon sex," as Tony calls it—and then the apple of William Tell and nationalism, and then the apple which fell on Sir Isaac Newton's head and started science.

When science has discovered something more,
We shall be happier than we were before.

But, in the meanwhile, the four of them pretty well cover the country, don't you think? I remember, last September, driving through Sedgemoor with Margaret and singing Christina Rosetti's song about the apple tree at the top of my voice. She said to me, "Uncle Peter, why are apples so awfully important?" You can tell her now.

In great haste. I have got to go off now and get drunk with Tony, but it isn't often that I think of anything, so I wrote and told you about this before I had forgotten it.

Love, Peter

P.S. I am also always rather fond of the apple that got inside George III's apple-dumpling.

P.P.S. Do you know what the apple which fell on Sir Isaac's head was? It was a "Maid of Kent"—now extinct.

17

March 5, 1942.

My dear,

You will keep on asking me about the sound religious upbringing of your remarkable children, and

> *Though the compliment implied*
> *Fills me with legitimate pride*
> *Still it cannot be denied*
> *That it has its inconvenient side.*

There was only one absolutely sensible thing that I ever heard said about religion, and that was said by Jake, the old darky, who used to scythe the fields at St. Matthew outside Louisville. The minister asked him if he believed in baptism, and he answered, "Why sure, boss, I seen it done." (Time out for crying like a pig, when I think of Kentucky all going on and us not there.)

Of course, if they are going to be troubled with religious doubt, like "John Grubby, who was short and stout," and want the answers to all the points and the evidence for the authenticity of the Gospels and all that, there is no one in England that they can better go to than to George. The amount that he taught me, after it had all been kept from me throughout all my careful religious upbringing, is immense, but, if you say that Martin and George do not quite click, I think that I can tell you why.

Martin is a poet—a little bit by performance—a good deal by temperament. He is neither a metaphysician nor a historian, and evidential difficulties do not particularly bother him. His danger is much more likely to be that of *"Video meliora proboque; deteriora sequor."*

Now, what I would say in criticism of George's religion is that it tends to be a little too exclusively a mere metaphysical argument. I remember once getting rather tight in his room on mulled claret in front of a hot fire. I went to sleep, and, when I woke up, George was saying, "And so, my dear Peter, eighthly, or h." There does not appear in his conversation much sense of a Voice that could speak to him with an authority greater than that of his own speculations—much sense that it was, perhaps, the plan—that we should not be able to understand, in order that we might ask for the fuller vision. When I hear George explaining things, I am always a little tempted, in my most unpardonably unregenerate moments, to say, "George, you've got it all so clear that I really wonder that it was worth while having a Revelation at all." (I have never said this, and I hope that I never shall, but I am confessing the sin before I commit it. I am sure that is the modern, scientific principle of insurance, a sort of spiritual Beveridge plan.)

In the same way, I have no doubt that George says his prayers with the utmost piety and regularity. But he does not seem to me a praying type. I do not quite know what he thinks happens when he prays. (Why don't they take a Gallup poll to find out how many people in England really think that anything happens? That would be interesting to know.) Dean Inge once said of Ruskin that he knew the use of everything in a church except the altar. That, again, seems to me a bit like George.

Now, different people are frightfully different about that sort of thing—I mean, even different religious people. I remember Michael Paravane once telling me that he had done something or other that the Catholics call a mortal sin and, for the moment at any rate, was in no mind to repent of it. (I suppose that I ought not to tell you all this, but, anyway, here goes.) Well, he was kneeling at the back of the Downside church at Benediction, with all the boys of the school in front of him, and he felt that it was absolutely intolerable to be separated from them. I thought that damned silly. Either he was right or wrong, and what possible difference could it make—the stinking boys being there anyway? I said to him, "That does not prove that you believe; it only proves that you want to belong." Of course, he would not agree, and it is certainly true of the Catholic Church—I am not quite sure if it is good or bad—that it has a curious hold over its people; not only bad people, but people who do not seem to believe half the things it teaches, yet prefer to obey off and on the rules that they think nonsense, so as to keep one foot in the camp rather than break with her altogether.

Now, I suppose that that is because they have a great sense that there is a channel from outside the world by which strength comes to one in this world, and that it would be folly to block up that channel. Well, Martin is not, I think, the least attracted by Rome, but he has that sense very strongly. He is very much of a sacramentalist.

He is no fool and can reason well enough. But reasoning about religion, without taking full advantage of all the privileges which religion offers, would seem to him a fool's game, like playing cricket left-handed in a ladies' match. Reason cannot be a substitute for experience. It needs experience on which to build and from which to argue. As he once said to me, you can only understand it from within.

I say all this as the case for Martin. Don't think that I ever have dreamed, or ever should dream, of suggesting to him that he give himself airs at George's expense. Of course, there is the other side to it. There are a thousand things that he, like all of us, could most profitably learn from George, and one of the reasons why he does not learn is that he is lazy. We certainly do not want to turn him into a sort of ecclesiastical Bunthorne.

Why, what an exceptionally pure young man
That pure young man must be.

Besides, I doubt if he can quite make that grade yet awhile, and I am unregenerate enough to be extremely glad that he cannot. The last thing that we want is

platitudes
In stained-glass attitudes.

Yours, Peter

18

My dear,

I don't seem to get my point quite right and, doubtless, am not fair either to George or to Martin. Tony once told me that I suffered from an excess of charity, floating upon a prurient imagination, and was always inventing sins that nobody had ever dreamed of committing, simply to have the pleasure of forgiving them. Perhaps there was something in it. Anyway, it is certainly true that, for the moment, Martin is quite satisfactorily un-Bunthornean. He picked up at one of those odd parties, the other day, a charming little brunette refugee, who was, he told me, a Basque, and for a week he would do nothing except talk about Roncesvalles and quote the Song of Roland:

> *Then ride they—how proudly, O God, they ride*
> *With rowels dashed in their coursers' side,*

he used to keep on saying from morning to night till I could brain him. Then, last night, he came bursting in here in a state of slightly chagrined hysterics. It appeared that it was all a misunderstanding, due to the fact that they could only converse in French, at which both of them very definitely spoke "ful faire and fetisly, after the scole of Stratford-atte-Bowe." She was not Basque at all. Her patience exhausted, she had suddenly burst out: "I do not know that country. I am Grik." Things, apparently, had not passed off quite smoothly, and I am afraid that that is the end of that romance, such as it was. Perhaps it was as well. Martin had tried to be apologetic over his mistake, but I fear that he suffers from the very conventional English failing that he simply cannot believe that it really matters what sort of a foreigner a foreigner is. I gather that she had flared up a bit and smacked his face for him when he had laughed about it. "She is a bit of a bitch really," he said. Maybe she is, but her annoyance seems a little more reasonable than Martin is disposed to allow.

I was reading Lucas' *Diary Under the Terror* last night in bed. He has what seems to me a curious point of view. He objects to a young man doing a cross-word puzzle, on the ground that it is a waste of time—as indeed it is. But then he says that he (Lucas) does not believe in a future life. Therefore, he grudges any time that is not spent in equipping his mind with the greatest of the achievements of the human genius. But, if you are to go out like a candle in a few years' time, what can it matter if this *animula, vagula, blandula,* before its extinction, loved Shakespeare and Beethoven rather than Nat Gould and "You're My Baby"? Besides, there is a paradox about all these Best Thoughts as a substitute for religion, since almost all the Best Thoughts were in one way or another speculations or affirmations about religion. Apparently, to such a man as Lucas, Dante was just a Thinker with a great, big capital T—such a good Thinker that one falls down and worships him and never dreams of paying any attention to what he thought.

But then, of course, it is easy enough to find excuses for futility on any philosophy. If we have all eternity before us, what can be the hurry? Why not do cross-word puzzles now? I suppose that the best practical thing to believe in is a future life, in which our fate depends on our conduct in this life. For pragmatic purposes, it is no good pitching the punishments too steep, because then, people, with their incurable optimism, think that God cannot be as bad as all that, and they will get round it somehow. If I were God, I would have a good deal of purgatory and very little hell and make the evidence of what is coming to us a lot plainer than it is at present—but then, of course, I am not God.

And that is, I do feel, the solid point. In the riot of subjective modernism we all waste our time in arguing about what we would do if we were God. (That is really what all this modern thought amounts to.) The whole question is of very secondary importance. Martin is quite right in wanting to get hold of some objective facts to bite on—that there is a God, that He is present in the Sacrament, that there is a channel by which we can receive His grace, that this is His plan, whether we entirely understand it or not—and he is quite right to ask, as the first question about all millenial schemes, whether Shelleyan or Marxian, what evidence there is that they are ever going to be realised? If it is never going to happen anyway, discussions about the precise technique that the lion will employ in order to lie down with the lamb are merely boring. The whole question is, in the last analysis, a question of fact, not a question of values, and I envy Martin his certainty—the more so, in that I cannot wholly share it.

People talk about religious education and say what a terrible thing it is that there is so little of it, but, in one way, it is a terrible thing that there is so much of it. Everyone is in a panic now—as well they might be—at the amount of sheer wickedness that there is loose in the world, and a lot of people are clamouring for religious education to put it right. As a result, many more people to-day believe in religious education than believe in religion. There are dangers in that. There is the obvious danger of the State using the Church as a policeman in Napoleonic fashion, but there is a deeper danger. Christian morality and secular morality do not quite coincide, even if we take secular morality at its highest and purest. The Church does, in extreme cases, demand of its faithful that it do things which, if we were to look only to this world, it would be unreasonable to do. For instance, whatever the exact line that one draws about divorce, could one honestly argue that on purely secular grounds divorce should never be allowed? The religious case must be defended on religious grounds. The attempt to defend it on secular grounds, however lofty, inevitably involves cheating and special pleading.

Yours, Peter

19

My dear,

I am sorry that you do not like Martin's Betty. Do not be too fussy. One cannot be over-choosy with the young these days. There are certain advantages in a married woman rather older than oneself with a taste for philosophising. It cannot in the nature of things go right, and it is not very likely in the nature of things to go very wrong. As I told Martin, the worst that is likely to happen is that the husband may come down one day in a fury and horsewhip him, and that would not do any particular harm to any one. But he said that the husband was a very long way off—Burma or Inverness or Golders Green—I forget exactly where.

Let us face the facts a little more seriously. I quite see the points of your indictment of the girl. She obviously is not at all a good wife in the conventional pattern; she admits as much herself. I do not mean in the least that she is unfaithful in the technical sense. I should not think that she is that for a second. Rather the opposite. Her whole trouble is that she is genuinely mannish, and the whole notion of sex, whether in connection with her husband or any other man, is repugnant to her.

You know that line of Dante that I am always boring you by quoting, and, still more, by expounding: "Ladies

83

that have intelligence of love." I should say that Betty, like a good many other modern women, is an exact example of a lady who has no intelligence of love—who does not understand what it is about, and who has no notion of the meaning of a union of two wills—and that is, admittedly, a pretty big gap. But, at least, she is not of that awful type that knows everything about sex and nothing about love. The real point about free love is that it is not love at all—it is of the essence of love that it demands to bind itself. Love is, of its nature, in that sense unfree. But, anyway, that is not Betty's trouble. She does not want free love; she only wants freedom instead of love—which is simpler.

So what? So she ought not to have married. Fairly obviously—but that's done now. If she had been of heroic sanctity, having made her mistake, she would have set her teeth, told no one, and gone through with it. I doubt if it would have succeeded, unless her husband was a very goofy man, but, anyway, you have got to allow for an upbringing in which nobody talked about heroic sanctity, and everybody talked about her right to live her own life. She is not altogether to be blamed if she took her abominable education at its word.

Of course, it is all complicated by the fact that she rather likes her husband in every capacity except that of her husband. There is nothing that she will not do for him except love, honour and obey him, and he, silly noodle, pretends to believe all this same sort of stuff that she believes and says that, if she wants to go and join the A.T.S. and have a career of her own, then she has what he calls a right to do so. But I am trying to straighten out their confusions, not to entangle them in worse confusions.

All this feminism seems to me to be cursed with an absurd contradiction. If the well-being of the State is the most important thing in the world, then our greatest national need is a higher birth-rate, and the most certain of all statistics is that the more education women have, the fewer their children. Therefore, the greatest political need of the day is less higher education for women. Yet, though woman's place in general is in the home, there are some women who are not interested in children and are interested in careers. It is madness to encourage women to be like that, but, where they are like that without encouragement, then a free society must provide a niche for them. I am not as anti-feminist as you are; men seldom are as anti-feminist as women. Men do not mind having women Members of Parliament. It is women who refuse to vote for them. It is feminists that I object to, more than feminism; I think that I would give votes to all women who could prove that they were never suffragettes.

Seriously, I do not think that disliking Betty helps a whole lot. So far as she is arrogant and thinks herself the last word in progress, one can hardly help but dislike her. But she does not really think that—at any rate, in her quieter moments. Perhaps I am a little biased by the fact that she embarrassed me by bursting into tears yesterday in my office. But I think that she does genuinely see herself as a problem—"made odd," as she put it. She does not ask that everybody should be like her, but she does ask:

"Being as I am, what am I to do? I know that I am not a good wife, and I ought to look after Jackie, instead of running round joining things, but what am I to do?"

You see, Ruth, you live down at Barston in a kind of oasis of sense, and I do not think that you quite allow for the complete madness of the modern world. People have passed beyond the stage in which they reject the principles by which civilisation has stood for ten thousand years, into a stage in which they have not heard of them. I do not think that Betty had ever met anybody who talked sense about anything, until she met Martin. It is natural enough that you, as a mother, should worry about her effect on Martin, but there is the other side of it— Martin's effect on her. I do not really think that it does Martin much harm to go about with her, and I am sure that it does her no end of good to go about with Martin. You cannot think of the effect that a young man can have these days who, without shouting about it or preaching about it, quietly makes it clear, with every sentence he speaks, that he thinks that bunk is bunk.

The person who is really after her is not Martin, but the old general. I took her in to see him one morning, and he spent all the next day telephoning round and round the War Office in an erotic frenzy, to sign her up as his P.A. She was not playing one little bit. Let that be your comfort. If that is what happens to a major general, what has a penniless young gentleman cadet to fear—or hope?

Yours, Peter

20

My dear,

What a lot of nasty cracks! "I know that you don't mind, because you never mind anything." "Charity, thy name is indolence." I bare my back. All that you say is a half-truth. (That is my regular gambit. If you say that a charge is a lie, you have to prove it so, and, if you say it is true, you have to abandon your position. But, if you say it is a half-truth, you can slip out of answering the charge and still stick to your prejudices.) Still, I do honestly think that this is a half-truth. Pascal said that all man's troubles came from his inability to live in one room, and I do think that most of the things that people do they do out of pure restlessness, and it would be much better if they were left undone. I am convinced that the human race would be much happier if only it were a little lazier. The one proposition on which all politicians of all parties agree as a platitude is that the object of politics is to raise the standard of living of the people. And yet, if we compare the poor with the rich, or one nation with another, or, so far as literature and art enable us to do so, one age with another, all the evidence would seem to show that material standard of living had very little bearing on happiness. It is curious to note that the only two politicians in the modern world who do not offer their followers a higher standard are Gandhi and de Valera. Neither of them are unmixed heroes of mine, but they are the two politicians who have held on longest to the leadership of their parties. And, as for the bearing of prosperity on virtue, I do not know which is the more unscriptural— the ambition of the rich to remain rich, or the ambition of the poor to become so. The whole teaching of the Gospels, surely, is that one is very lucky to be poor and very unlucky to be rich.

But I quite agree that the Gospel is, in one way and in all seriousness, a very dangerous document. There is— I will not say a half, but at least a quarter—truth in Dr. Johnson's, "Sir, no man can be more innocently employed than in making money"—perhaps the most profoundly anti-Christian remark in human history. Of course, even supposing that he be making money innocently, there are many ways in which he can be more innocently employed than in making it—saying his prayers, for instance, visiting the sick, looking at the sunset, reading poetry, composing music. But, anyway, is innocence enough? It is a very negative quality. He should be employing his time profitably—in some task that has in it some hint of the abiding truths, that has, as Hamlet would put it, "some relish of salvation in it."

Granted that that is what he should be doing—what St. Francis of Assisi would be doing—but is it what Tom Smith, of 23 Laburnum Manor, would be likely to be doing? It is not true that he could not be more innocently employed than in making money, but it is profoundly true that he might be, and often is, a great deal less innocently employed than in making it. That is the quarter-truth in Johnson's remark. The danger, as I am well aware, in the teachings of the Gospel, Pascal, Peter Hartington-Smith, and other such eminent spiritual authorities is this. It is possible that some of their less eminent disciples, lacking the profound mystical gifts of the masters, will say: "It is obvious that this world is only dust and ashes and not worth bothering about. So let us do damn all"—a somewhat negative conclusion. Roman Catholics, for instance, are, obviously, on the whole lazier than other people in business. I once asked Michael Paravane why. He said that it was not a point in favour of Catholics, but it was a point in favour of Catholicism. It was what you would expect if a true religion was preached to rather dim people.

There are, it seems to me, four stages of man from this point of view, if one sets it all out in Jacques-like form. Starting from the bottom, there is first the man who bothers about nothing, human or divine, and leaves his room unswept through utter indolence. Then there is the man who sweeps the room simply because he thinks it important that rooms should be clean. Then there is the man who says: "I have an immortal soul and will soon be dead anyway. What can it matter whether rooms are swept or not?" Finally, there is George Herbert's man, who, as it were, comes back to the tasks of the world from the contemplation of the eternal verities and performs them because they are his tasks, doing with all his might whatever his right hand findeth to do.

Who sweeps a room as for Thy laws,
Makes that and the action fine.

But this, doubtless, as the old dons who wrote Greek grammars used to say, is very rare.

Now, Martin's danger, if you really want me to speak frankly about him, seems to me the danger of what I may call "indolence through faith." A good proportion of the warnings which it is conventional for pastors and masters and mothers and uncles to issue to their adolescent hopefuls are quite unnecessary to him. He may, perhaps, in time, shift his religious opinions, for better or for worse, on this or that detail, but there is not the smallest danger that he will, as the Victorians used to say, "lose his faith" —that he will suddenly meet some frightfully clever man who will prove to him that the whole Christian system is a Mithraic myth, and rush shouting from the room into the embraces of the Ethical Church. On the contrary, all his Oxford pals—to say nothing of the clergymen at Trumpinghurst—were, of course, agnostics of one kind or another; he knew all their points and had the completest contempt for them. He thought of himself—perhaps a bit too complacently—as a person who had a sense of colour in a world of the colour-blind. And, as for writers, he is the only person whom I have ever met who has accomplished a feat which I have hitherto considered impossible—that of underrating the intelligence of intellectuals.

The Christian religion is a very tough nut. It takes a good three generations permanently to disbelieve it.

People with religious parents—I mean sincerely religious parents who base all their thinking on religion, not just nominal conformists—may kick over the traces for a time, pass through phases, blaspheme and struggle, but it always gets them again in the end. It gets them because they cannot help themselves, but argue and think in Christian terms, and, if you argue in Christian terms, then you find in the end that Christianity has the better of the argument. It has the metaphysics and it has the poetry and it has the history. The only way to escape from it is to be ignorant of it, and Martin can never escape that way, even if he wanted to. He has been too well educated—I mean, of course, at home, not at school.

But I do detect in him a certain danger that the very vigour of his faith may be to him a temptation to idleness. Christianity, I sometimes think, is a very dangerous religion to those who are not saints. I am not thinking of the moment of "*Video meliora proboque; deteriora sequor.*" That is a surrender to unreason, frankly confessed. The crude challenge of an act clearly defined as a mortal sin is, in some ways, less insidious than the danger of flopping about and spending hours in gossiping and drinking and lolling on sofas and "doing things rather more or less," on the argument that nothing is really worth doing anyway.

> *Dr. Clifford*
> *And I have differed;*
> *He disapproves of sin*
> *But I disapprove of gin.*

I have always had a sneaking feeling that there was something to be said for Dr. Clifford. I did not particularly blame Martin for despising the other undergraduates at Oxford, and I did not particularly blame him for wasting his time in their company. But it should have been one or the other. I did blame him for both despising them and wasting his time with them. His danger is, perhaps, that he is a little bit too much "at ease in Zion."

I used to say that he might turn out an even better bat than Bobby, because he was less nervous, but now I am not sure whether it is that he is less nervous or that he cares less. Of course, one might say: Why should he care? Why should he not enjoy his cricket? Why should he not slog about a bit if he wants to—particularly in these days, when there is no first-class cricket to aim at? No reason at all why he should not, if he wants to. But does he really want to? Has it ever been known in nature that a man who could play first-rate cricket really wants to play second-rate cricket? If he plays second-rate cricket, is it not a sure proof that some leaden lump of accidie has somehow found its unlovely way into his soul?

I do not want to be too unutterably pedagogical, but the real trouble about Martin, both at the end of his time at Trumpinghurst and at Oxford, was that he did no work —a disease by no means original and not necessarily mortal. I, on the whole, welcomed this rather absurd Betty episode, about which you were quite properly concerned, because, while, on the one hand, I did not fear any very serious complications; on the other hand, Martin did undoubtedly make a little bit of a fool of himself—and it is very good for a young man to learn that he cannot carelessly ride superb over all the fences of life and proudly dismiss those which he neglects as not worth jumping. However important may be poetic vision and dialectical ability, courage and courtesy, devotion and piety, it remains that the root virtue is humility.

Humility is the first of all virtues for many reasons— and, not least, for this paradoxical reason, that, if combined with humility, a certain sort of pride which were otherwise odious becomes, instead, a virtue. Martin seems to be doing much better as a soldier at his O.C.T.U. than ever he did as an undergraduate at Oxford. He will make, I fancy, a damned good officer, and the root reason why he is a good soldier is, if I diagnose rightly, this: It is natural to him to be smart and efficient and physically competent and know what he is supposed to know. He likes being liked. Now, that is not the highest of motives for action, and, in that mixture of the Spiritual Exercises with the Camelious Hump in which he tended to move through Oxford, he would perhaps have dismissed the notion of acting from such a motive with scorn. Humility has, I think, now taught him the important lesson that fairly good people should be glad enough, if, on occasion, they find that they are acting from fairly good motives.

Does this all help?

Love, Peter

21

My dear,

If you want to go back to feminism and Betty, of course, I am on the side of the angels—that is to say, on your side. The only request that I would make is that you be careful not to substitute a new totalitarianism of the normal for the opposite totalitarianism of the abnormal. I agree that the normal woman wants to have children—especially after she has had them—and I agree, therefore, that those who get hold of young girls and put into their heads the notion that they are happier having careers are indeed the enemies of the people. But what of the oddities—who undoubtedly do exist—of those, like Betty, who, apart from any schoolma'am's suggestions, do not want to have children?

I, of course, agree with you that, if there are many like that, the country collapses—and probably their number is on the increase. Their number is on the increase because, certainly in Betty's case and, I suspect, in most cases, such people are as they are because they are the children of unhappily married parents. They have a repulsion to the family because from their earliest memory "family" has meant to them, not what it meant to us, but a place of strain and quarrelling. Unhappy marriages in one generation mean childless marriages in the next. But, although all that may be true, it does not answer my practical question. If there are people like that, what are we to do about them? It is not helpful merely to tell them that they ought to have had different sorts of grandmothers.

Politically, I am afraid that what I really in my heart of hearts believe is that, whatever may be done to mitigate the evil, it is almost a law of nature that, whenever you get a higher standard of living and what is called civilisation, women have wider interests and, therefore, fewer children. The population falls, and the ruder, more fecund barbarians break in and overrun, to become in their turn civilised and decadent and, in the end, overthrown. That has happened a dozen times in history, and I am afraid that all the signs are that it is history's all but inevitable law, and that there is every likelihood that it will happen again in the not very distant future. The only question is: Which barbarians will win? Is this Spengler? I am not quite sure. I never read him. But what is more important is: Is it true?

Of course, it is possible that Christianity has a unique preservative value which no other faith has ever had. Through Christianity, Rome did in a measure survive her own death, and there was a continuity between the world of the Middle Ages and the world of the Empire. It may be that this power from beyond the world will again lead us through our new Dark Ages. But I would not myself bet too heavily on that. Either Christianity is true or it is not true. If it is not true, then there is no reason to think that its effect will be unique. If it is true, then we

must face the fact that there is no word among the re-
corded sayings of Christ, no hint among the survivals of
the beliefs of the early Church, that Christ came in any
way to save what is known as civilisation. To the contrary. "My kingdom is not of this world," and the Christian seems to be instructed to expect to live among the
collapsing ruins of all secular edifices.

How much does what men call the collapse of civilisation matter? That it is very inconvenient for those upon
whom it collapses, that the suffering will indeed be overwhelming is, alas, self-evident. But whether, after the collapse, the generations that never knew anything but barbarism are more or less happy than the generations that
never knew anything but civilisation, whether men were
happier or less happy in the ninth century than in the
nineteenth is very uncertain. I suspect that it will prove
that there is very little in it.

I know that a single instance cannot justify a generalisation, but do you remember how Pepys says that he was
woken up in the middle of the night by an old man snoring, and he thought the experience almost unbelievably
funny? "But, Lord, the mirth it caused me to be waked
in the night, by this snoring round me; I laughed till I
was ready to burst!" Can we imagine anyone in the twen-
tieth century getting joy out of hearing a man snore? A
certain gusto for what Browning called

The mere living . . . fit to employ
The heart and the soul and the senses for ever in joy

seems to have gone out of life with the coming of the complexities of civilisation, and *taedium vitae* has taken its place.

But that is all, perhaps, a far cry from Betty. Of her, I think that she can within reason be pitied, but I agree with you that she ought not to be encouraged. But then, poor girl, I do not think that she is encouraged—certainly not in any company in which I have ever seen her—certainly not by Martin, by whom she is very definitely more grinned against than grinning—to her own surprise, chagrin, and, I hope, advantage.

Love, Peter

22

November 4, 1942.

My dear,

I suppose that Martin must have gone back from his embarkation leave last week, and I daresay that he has left the country—or, at any rate, will be leaving any day now. I feel that I must write you a line, and yet it is difficult to know what to say that can be of much value. You see, my dear, you are a very difficult person to lie to. It is no good serving up to you the "easy speeches that comfort cruel men," or, indeed, "the cruel speeches that comfort easy men." It is no good telling you fatuously and without reason that Martin will be all right and pretending that people do not get killed in war—for you know, alas, that that is not true.

> Life, to be sure, is nothing much to lose
> But young men think it is, and we were young.

Nor is it very much good preaching to you of the glories of the cause, for neither you nor I, alas, believe very much in the cause as it is commonly preached to us to-day by our organs of refined opinion. When Bobby was killed, the war still meant something. It was then still England and France against Germany, sustained by the friendly support of Russia; and England and France, with all their faults, did believe in the rule of law, and Germany and Russia most emphatically did not and most emphatically believed in its overthrow. But now we have quite a different kettle of fish. People say that Hitler's blunder in attacking the Russians has won us the war. Obviously, it has been enormously to our short-term advantage, and I cannot blame our leaders, seeing the straits that we were in, for catching at what straws of salvation they could. But, if it has won us the war, it has also largely made nonsense of the war.

What an extraordinary and hateful war this war is! An ideological war indeed! Never in history has there been a more atrocious war—that is, a war in which men were more bestial to one another, and, yet, can anyone show any coherent difference between the ideas of the one side and those of the other—I mean between the ideas of the Russians and those of the Germans? After all this *bombinatio in vacuo*, in which people shout at one another about right-wing and left-wing, I really cannot for the life of me see the smallest difference between them. Every day our precious ideologies seem to differ more and more about less and less. In the old days right-wing used to mean traditionalist and left-wing used to mean anti-traditionalist. As long as that persisted, there was a meaning in the distinction, but between the modern right-wings and left-wings there seems no difference at all. It is just a gang in power, and the only question is, which gang? It matters as little as it matters which lot of gangsters may be for the moment in control in a city.

Of course, we, with all our faults, are better than that. We do stand for the rule of law—which is the one thing that matters, and there are some jolly optimists who think that we must vindicate our virtue by going on to clean up the Russians after we have finished with the Germans. It may be that we shall have to. Who can tell what will prove necessary in this world of lunacy? But, if so, it is far from certain how much of a rule of law would emerge even from our victory. What happens in a war? Shakespeare knew. "Laertes wounds Hamlet; then, in scuffling, they change rapiers, and Hamlet wounds Laertes," says the stage direction—and they continue until both are killed. The trouble with an ideological war is that, whichever side wins, the worst idea always wins.

Chrétiens ont droit, paiens ont tort may be true as a metaphysical proposition, but as a military proposition

99

the Christians do not conquer the pagans until they have first reduced themselves to the morals of the pagans. What then? Do I look forward to a world absolutely without hope? Do I condemn the war as a complete futility? No, I do not do that. Wars are horrible affairs, and the hope that out of them a new heaven and a new earth will emerge is a hope of lunatics. Of their nature, war aims, so far as they are sane, can only be negative; wars can prevent something, and, sometimes, evil as they are, they may be necessary to prevent a greater evil. The world is never a better place at the end of a war than it was at the beginning. But it may have become less bad as a result of a war than it would have done without it. I should say that that was true of this war. We could go on arguing for ever about what mistakes were made in the twenty years between the wars. But, at least, in September, 1939, a certain situation existed, and in that situation what could we do but fight? And, still more, on the day of Dunkirk what could we do but fight? If we were fighting to build a better world, our success is problematical. But, if we were fighting to prevent the invasion of England, to save ourselves from concentration camps, then we have succeeded, and it was well worth succeeding. So now we go on fighting, and Martin goes on fighting, because we must. Peace is not an immediate possibility. There is no room in the world both for Hitler and for us. So we must continue until Hitler is eliminated.

And, to those who say that we are only putting Hitler down in order to put Stalin up, I can only answer that we have no alternative but to put Hitler down whatever the consequences. I was not one of those who wanted war with Hitler. It would have been far better, had it been possible to avoid it, but it was not possible. So, Stalin, however much he may be the enemy of law, is not now threatening to invade us—nor, indeed, at the moment, in a position to invade anybody. The day may come when he starts invading people. If so, we shall have to take that fence when we come to it. With Stalin, as with Hitler, I hope that we shall do all that we can to avoid a quarrel, if it is possible, and, if it is not possible, that will be just too bad.

I know that this is all fairly dreary, but I am afraid that the truth about European politics is fairly dreary. For four hundred years now we have preserved the policy of a balance of power, and what has been the result? Four hundred years of almost continual war. Every time our leaders tell us, "Just one more war, and then there will be peace," and the end of every war creates a situation which, itself, requires another war for its liquidation. In order to curb Spain, we built up France, and in order to curb France, we built up Prussia, and in order to curb Prussia, we are building up Russia, and, next, in order to curb Russia, we shall build up—whom? It certainly does not make a whole lot of sense—the less so, if we reflect that, in so far as the wars are for economic causes, everyone all round could obviously be much richer if there were no wars at all, and, in so far as they are for moral causes, every country always emerges from a war less moral than when it went into it.

But what comfort, you may say, is all this to me

when Martin goes off to the war? This: You are at the third remove. There is a first class who cannot reconcile themselves to suffering for a cause at all. There is a second class—the class of what I may call the snob sufferers— who can be reconciled to suffering for a cause, so long as that cause is high-sounding and large and glamorous and idealistic. I overheard an extraordinary piece of blasphemy from a young twenty-year-old platinum blonde at the War Office bar the other day. "Of course, no one would mind being crucified for the sins of the whole world," she said, "but just having to scrub the steps for Auntie—I ask you!"

Well, it is not for me to preach sermons on humility, on "the trivial round, the common task, which furnish all we need to ask." Let us put it not on a spiritual, but on a practical, plane. These grandiose plans do not come off. The world's great age does not begin anew. Millenial secularism is all bunk, but, on the other hand, if you are content to aim at small, concrete, practical goods, you can often achieve them. That, surely, is what Martin is achieving, if he does his bit as a sensible, efficient soldier. It is a very worthy achievement. I always like the simplicity of that epitaph on the men of Tegea in the Greek Anthology: "Because of the valour of these men the smoke did not come." What an admirable epitaph on a soldier! What a justification of him—or of a fireman, either, if it comes to that. The negative is so right. That is what valour is for—to stop things.

It is you that I am worrying about, not Martin. I am not going to be so foolish as to tell you the lie that he may not get killed, though, for by far the greater part of his time, he will certainly be in no greater danger than I am in the War Office; and it is quite likely that he may never hear a shot fired in anger at all. But, to tell the truth, mankind is, I think, in a rather beautiful conspiracy about the fear of death. Just because some few odd people mind a great deal, all the rest of us pretend to mind a lot more than we really do. I shall never forget standing in the trenches during a bombardment with the shells bursting round us one day at Easter, 1918. The chap next to me whispered:

"Peter, shall I tell you a secret?"

"Yes," I said.

"You'll promise not to tell anybody."

"Yes," I said.

"I don't mind this one little bit," he said.

That is just what I found with most people in London in the blitz. It may be that the horrors and terrors of modern life have brought their own recompense. Life is so much more miserable now than it ever was before that no one in the least minds leaving it—or it may be that it was always thus. I am not sure which. But, in any event, I think that very few people do mind much to-day. Life has become little more than a dentist's waiting-room, as we attend the call to the real business next door, and we would just as soon that the call came soon as late. A battle is boring, when you are out-bombed, out-gunned, out-fought in every way, but it is not so bad if it is anything approaching an equal fight, and rather fun when it is a victory. "How can man die better than facing fearful odds?" is a rhetorical exaggeration, but "how can man die better than facing reasonable odds?" would have been quite a fair question.

So, without wishing to be callous or cynical, I have no especial dose of pity for Martin. He likes soldiering. The odds against anything happening to him are reasonably heavy. I daresay that he will have quite a good time. It is you for whom I am sorry. It is the women at home for whom war is hell. It is no good telling you not to mind. It is no good demonstrating to you on philosophic principles that you need not mind. You must mind. You would be unhappy, if you were happy. You would feel that you had betrayed your trust and denied your nature—the mystery, I suppose, of motherhood, where the greatest pain is inextricably mixed up with the greatest joy, not only at the first physical beginnings, but throughout all life. It brings me back again to that eternal Betty that we are always arguing about. I told you that I had found her one day in a flood of tears, but I do not think that I told you why. I asked her why. "Because Jackie has gone to the front," she said, "and I don't mind a bit. I feel such a cad." The Epicureans thought that ataraxia was one of the fine requisites of a happy life. What fools they were!

God bless you, my dear. I am sure that it will be all right, and I know how useless in itself is all that I, or any-one else, can say. But, in a way, as I learnt at the time of Marjorie's death, the value of such words is in their futility. They are evidence, not that we can help, but that we want to help—of our impotence and our desire—evidence that we care.

The heart asks more than life can give;
When that is learned, then all is learned—

a truth and a terrifying mystery. Why were we made to care so much and then, thus caring, sent into a transient catastrophic world like this? And yet, a deeper mystery still—the world being as it is, would we have our hearts otherwise? Would we prefer not to care?

Love, Peter

23

February 15, 1943.

My dear,

You must take in that you and I are frightfully queer —perhaps because we are half Americans, perhaps for some other reason. We do not find it the least difficult to talk to anyone, whatever his educational background. We find it so little difficult, that we do not easily understand how difficult it is for many people. But it is difficult, and that difficulty is, I believe, the root difficulty of the rural problem. Snobbery, one loosely says, but I am not sure that snobbery is really the right word. Those who are most awkward in the presence of men who differ from them are often decently humble people, who in no way think themselves superior. They are tongue-tied because they are shy and do not know what to say. So, I, of course, entirely agree with all that you say about the follies of land nationalisation. It is obvious that all the alleged benefits of cooperation and cheap credit could be obtained just as well without nationalisation, and that an urban electorate would never stand for the beggarly two percent on its investment, which is all that the landlord expects to get back to-day. The case in economics is so overwhelming that it hardly bears arguing about, but that is not the real case. The real case is the existence of two nations—of two different ways of life—in rural England. Landlord and farmer and labourer must all live, but there is no reason why they should live in such fantastically different ways as they did until recently and, indeed, largely do still. That was never the way at Barston. It never even occurred to Bobby to live thus differently. He would have found life unbearably boring, had he done so. He always used to agree with Burton, who, you know, in his *Anatomy of Melancholy* says very sensibly that his one real cure for melancholy was to listen to the bad language of the Oxford bargees. But distance is still the way in most places.

Of course, I criticise from outside. I have not got the dirt under my finger-nails in the way that you have. People talk about adult education, but nobody can really learn anything after he is grown up. Or, at least, he can only learn along the lines upon which he had begun to learn at a time before he could remember. There is a legal fiction that education begins at five. In reality it has finished then. So I, who was not brought up on a farm as you were, can never really think as a farmer, as you do and as your children do.

"Ho," I say to the cows, and, when they pay no attention, "Can't you hear me say 'Ho'?" But they know. It does no good.

"Side-bearing oats," says Robert solemnly to Billy Perkins.

"Yes, Mr. Robert," says Billy.

"After fallow?" asks Robert, raising his eyebrows.

"The ground's a bit fine, but we could not help ourselves," says Billy.

"Oats would do best after a white-straw crop," says Robert.

"Oh, they'll not do so badly," says Billy.

Now I could never talk like that to such a man as Billy Perkins, if I lived to be a hundred. Even if I knew all the stuff, I should not have the face to say it in that offhand way.

That is why I think it so frightfully good for your children and mine to have been brought up on the farm. Town tastes, if they need be picked up at all, can easily be picked up later in life, but country tastes, if they are not learned in infancy, are not learnt at all. But do not worry too much if, as they grow up, they a little wish to flutter their wings—Martin talking about the delights of Mediterranean life—Margaret, all in the modern fashion, saying, "I will not be dictated to" and going off to become a stenographer—even, perhaps, should Robert in time lose his heart to something more nearly human than a cow. That is the way of the world.

When I was at Coventry, I shared digs for a time with a chartered accountant from Glasgow, and he taught me, what I believe to be true, that all achievement in life is the result of withdrawal and return. What he called the period of achievement was a short one. "Christ, for instance," he said, "with the greatest of all works to do, prepared for thirty years for a ministry of three years. There was none of the vulgar modern impatience to get down to it." So, with lesser mortals, they have the seeds of their destiny, the shape of their life, sown in them in infancy. Man can only learn by contrast. It is only right that they should wander off for a short time in the first years of growth to different lands and different activities. None but a fool would be surprised if curiosity during those years should sometimes lead them into folly. But men and women return, in the end, whence they came. We encompass the world, only to learn that there is no place like home—that is to say, people who have been brought up, as our children have, not only to live in the country, but to love country things. If they have been brought up in the country, complaining that there are not enough buses to get them into the cinema—brought up like townees in exile from a town—you can hardly expect them to wish to return home, or, indeed, to be contented anywhere.

Yours ever, Peter

P.S. I believe that only one percent of people have normal eyesight. In the same way, only about one percent have normal standards, but your children are very lucky that you are of that one percent. Chaucer was another—a very good poet, don't you think?

24

March 17, 1943.

My dear,

I am indeed delighted about Martin's M.C. I am one of those, as you know, who are a little sceptical about the war, but who like good soldiers. By all means do everything that one can to prevent a war, but, if it comes, I cannot see much point in personal pacifism, and, if one is going to be a soldier, I can see no point at all in being a bad soldier. Be a good soldier—of course in the fullest sense of the word "good"—not merely an efficient soldier, but also one who does what he can to see that the war is fought according to the so-called rules of war, to prevent even war itself from degenerating—and, above all, one who does what he can to prevent enmity developing into hatred.

The only thing that I really hate is hatred. The

fashion these days is to try and see everything from God's point of view—to ask Kantian questions whether it would be well for the whole world if every one were acting as I am acting now—to answer Thomist questions about the conditions of a just war. I cannot think that it works out very well in practice. It is all very well for political and ecclesiastical leaders, perhaps, to ask such questions, but, when schoolboys and undergraduates and, indeed, people like you and me ask them, the only effect is to make us pacifist until the day before war is declared and to delay our determination to resist aggression until the aggression has already happened and it is too late to prevent the war. The only result of academic pacifism is to persuade the aggressors that the victims will not fight and thus to make war more probable. Joad breeds Ribbentrop, in an ideological, if not in a biological, sense.

"Ah, yes," say the admirable wiseacres, "but suppose that everybody threw down his arms and refused to fight." It would be delightful! But nature does not make leaps. All the world has never been converted suddenly to any cause, and the real, practical question, therefore, is, "Suppose that half the people, or half the nations, threw down their arms and refused to fight?" In that case the only result would be that the gangsters would swipe everything that they wished.

Pale Ebenezer thought it wrong to fight,
But Roaring Bill who bashed him thought it right.

I perfectly agree that very few things are worth fighting for—that, before all demands, one ought to ask, "Is it not better to let them have it than to suffer all the evils of war?" But do not let us be under any delusion that they will take it, whatever it is, and be content. Do not let us imagine that the gangsters will be at once converted by the beauty of the pacifists' moral life and surrender all their ill-gotten gains. Let us even admit, for the sake of argument, if you will, that the moral lives of all pacifists are absolutely beautiful, but, even so, we must remember that the Crucifixion did happen.

The deepest truths are doubtless to be found in Christian resignation, but even the old pagan fatalism has a dignity and a beauty that is denied to this modern fuss to find out "who's to blame?" One can settle the blame for small, simple things. If somebody leaves the garden gate unlocked, we can, perhaps, find out whose fault it was. If somebody bumps off Mrs. Snooks, we can, perhaps, discover, if not whose fault it was, at least who dun it. But on these larger matters, it is surely an impudence for any one less than God to pass judgment. You remember how Helen was ranting away in her egoistic self-vanity. It was she who had caused all the war. She was "a bitch." Let them do with her whatever they wanted. (One feels rather self-important when confessing that one has made a war.) But old Priam will have none of it. He says:

This is the high gods' doing. I lay not blame on thee.
They sent us this war from Achaea with all its misery.

If only people could think like that now! How infinitely far the world has degenerated in three thousand years!

Well, I must say that I think it is refreshing virtue

in Martin that he does not seem to take the least interest in the war—I mean, in the political causes of the war. Nobody ought to have political opinions until he has first learnt something about life and grappled for himself with the problem of earning a living. Political undergraduates are an abomination. I would close the Debating Societies down if I had my way. If Martin has got to fight in a war, the only sensible plan is to treat it as a gigantic cricket-match, and I like his touch of waving at the Germans before he fired at them. Of course, the Germans are by no means the decent fellows that he likes to think them. Martin's opinions of them, as opinions, are worthless. But they are the right opinions for a person to hold who has no knowledge and no pretension to knowledge. The first probability is that people are much of a muchness, even if they are not in this particular case.

It may be argued, perhaps, that it is necessary to hate in order to fight well. That may be true of some people—perhaps of most people. The secularist, with his prating of a perfect world just around the corner, has to be told, perhaps, that all man's wickedness is concentrated in some one nation or gang, which alone stands between him and the Lotus. But that is merely to say that a man who is a fool must also be an idiot. Martin does not need such a stimulus of folly. He does things decently just for the fun of doing them decently—"an excellent thing in soldiers," as King Lear might say. There is no getting over it that, when all the printers' ink has been spilled, there is no joy so great as that of the discovery of courage, and no quality so attractive in another.

I am so glad and only hope and pray, my dear, that fortune will continue to favour the brave. Africa is all right for him, but for you it's hell.

Love, Peter

25

April 13, 1943.

My dear,

I got back home late last night and found your telegram that Martin was missing. Oh, my dear, I am sorry. Of course I will do what I can at the War Office to find out any news, but I do not pretend that I can do much. The Vatican is the best source of information, particularly for Mediterranean fighting, and we must watch them. Don't give up hope. The situation is anything but hopeless. Apparently, he was missing on the 25th, and a number of prisoners were taken on that day as the Italians broke into our positions, and the Italians always take some time to sort out prisoners.

But, saying that, I know what the next days will be for you—the agony of waiting, when one feels that one could bear the worst, if only one knew the worst, and where hope alone is hopeless—intolerable, but yet will not be killed. And the trouble of writing to you is, I know, that you will not allow me to cheat—to pretend that chances are greater than they are, and I know, too, the great wisdom of your philosophy, which understands that there is a time when philosophy is unavailing, when consolation is intolerable,when Rachel is mourning for her children and will not be comforted, with "will" as the operative word. Doubtless, all that George said was wise and true, and a time will come when you are ready for it, but I see all too clearly that that time is not yet.

> Sometimes in wintry springs
> Frost, as a midnight breath,
> Comes to the cherry flowers
> And blasts their prime.
> So I with all my powers
> Unused on men or things
> Go down the wind to death
> And know no fruiting time.

If the worst has happened, do not try to call evil good until you are ready for it. Greet it at first frankly as evil, unabashed in pagan despair, and then a little later, perhaps, will come the time for reconciliation. In the meanwhile, the time has not yet come even for despair.

God bless you.

Peter

26

Oh my dear,

How lovely it is to be like Mr. Edwards! We spin out our careful efforts at philosophy and try to prove that all is for the best when it appears to be for the worst, and then we find that it is unnecessary, and that everything is all right after all. Oh, my dear, I am so glad. I do not know when I have been so happy in my life. Hurrah! Hurrah! Hurrah! I will come down to-morrow as soon as I can get away from this stinking office, and I will bring with me two bottles of sherry, three bottles of champagne, and a bottle of brandy—that is what I can raise. Then we will all get tiddly—not tight, but tiddly—(including George) and we will sing songs.

> *For surely a tremendous ghost,*
> *The brazen-lunged, the bumper filler,*
> *Still sings to an immortal toast*
> *The Misadventures of the Miller.*

(Do you remember that lovely phrase of the Ladies of Llangollen—how the people "sang many songs, all applicable to their situation"?) That is what we will do. The Vatican Radio gave it out that he was in the list of prisoners last night, and I verified it. It is quite certain.

In haste, Peter

27

April 22, 1943.

My dear,

If Martin is somewhere near "the city that looks like something in a missal," you can bet your boots that that means Siena. Where else could he mean? You know those Neroccios at Michael's that he used to like. They would have given him the idea. They have probably got some prison-camp somewhere up by Poggibonsi or San Gimignano. Tuscany—you remember the silver of the grapes and the gold of the corn and the sun shining on them and the wind blowing over them. Really, my dear, I almost find it in my heart to envy him—though Italy in fascist wartime is not, I daresay, quite the Italy that we knew.

I will tell you something, now that Martin is safe, that I did not think it quite kind to say when all was still doubtful. It is all very well for George to say how good the book of Job is. So it is, perhaps, if you look at it simply as a case of God versus Job. Job loses his wife and his possessions and gets boils, and then, after he has hung on for a bit, he gets a new wife and new possessions and loses his boils. Well, as the drunken Boer said at the funeral, "What could be fairer or more reasonable than that?" Nothing, perhaps, so far as Job is concerned, but it always seems to me a bit tough on the first wife. What do you think?

I am sure that the answer is that it is a mistake to try to bypass suffering with argument. We must accept it—accept it as a good and take it into ourselves, if we can. If we cannot rise to that, then be honest and accept it frankly as an evil. But, in any event, "suffering is the badge of all our tribe." And that is why I am more and more coming round to Bobby's view of Homer. He, alone of men, does not cheat. Cheating—by which I mean, for the moment, the self-conscious attempt to justify God's ways to man—begins with Aeschylus, and all the rest of the world has suffered from being post-Aeschylean. I do not say that it is not perfectly legitimate to make this attempt at justification, and that those who made it have not attained to many deep and subtle truths which Homer never knew. Nevertheless, there was an integrity at the dawn of all in Homer, where good was good and evil evil, which the world can never again recapture. The dead lie stark upon the battlefield, and, one by one, the camp fires of the rival hosts start up, and it reminds Homer of the first touches of the morning sun as it lights first this mountain-line and then that before the eyes of the lonely shepherd, who has watched for it through the night.

> *When all the winds are laid*
> *And every height comes out, and jutting peak*
> *And valley, and the immeasurable heavens*
> *Break open to the height.*

Well, my dear, what would you? Has the human race ever beaten that since? Is it likely to beat it?

But what I am coming to is this. I only noticed the other day that the Homeric hope is exactly the opposite of the Christian hope. Dante says, "This world is indeed pretty bloody, but in love we have the evidence of a future life." But Homer says "Love is only bearable, because death is coming, which will end all."

> *But deep be the earth of my grave-mound above*
> *me, ere the day*
> *I hear the sound of your crying, of your carry-*
> *ing away,*

says Hector to Andromache. (Of course, in point of fact, death does not end all for Achilles, but that is the *Odyssey* and a different story to the *Iliad*.)

The whole arrangement anyway round is, it seems to me, absolutely extraordinary. If there is not a future life, I cannot see why anybody should ever have thought of it; and, if there is one, it is extraordinary that the evidence for it is not better. However, as Robert once justly observed to me, "Surely, Peter, people have argued about that before."

I must stop now. The trouble about the sort of letters I write is that there is no reason why they should ever stop. Most people stop because, apparently, they do not like writing. But I would much sooner write than not write.

Love, Peter

28

May 17, 1943.

My dear Ruth,

I had the most frightfully boring week-end with Tony. He would go on and on talking—rot without end. The only way that I could think of to shut him up was to make him a bet.

"Why don't you ever read anything, Tony?" I asked.

"Oh, I can't read," he said, "that is to say, not books. You forget that I have been in Parliament now for some years, and in Parliament one gets out of the way of reading books. It comes of having such a lot of letters and two bars, and always popping out of one and into the other and all that."

"Have you ever read the Bible, Tony?" I asked him.

"Oh, yes," he said, "I used to read it as a crib when we did Greek Testament at school."

"But have you ever read it since?"

"Of course, not," he said. "Who ever heard of anyone reading the Bible when he was not at school?"

"Well, Tony," I said, "I'll bet you a fiver that you don't read through the Gospel of St. Matthew between now and bedtime."

"Done," he said, and he picked up the Bible.

"You dirty dog," he commented, after looking at it, "you've given me the longest one."

My hope was that, by this bet, I would keep him quiet for an hour or two, but it did not work out like that. He found it so interesting that he insisted on reading it all out loud.

"Good God, Peter," he said, illumination gradually dawning upon him, "this is all about Jesus Christ."

One forgets how short the Gospels are. The trouble was that he had plenty of time to read it all—or, at least, the greater part of it—out loud before bedtime. So I lost my bet and had the worst of both worlds.

I suppose that it does no good to make a fuss, but it does, I must confess, a little annoy me that people should be as ignorant as Tony. I do not much mind their being plain, plumb ignorant as I mind the absence of standards. He is even ignorant that he is ignorant. He still gaily and carelessly claims for himself all the consideration and prestige due to an educated man. The important thing is that people should know how much they know, and know when they are ignorant and not bluff. It is a sort of uncovenanted benefit in favour of humility that people who are not humble are crashing bores.

Love, Peter

29

My dear,

Of course I am well aware that being associated with Tony does me harm. So what? A willingness to be associated and to suffer harm seems to me the very test of integrity. What virtue is there in professing a friendship if it does not do you harm? I have known Tony and known what sort of a person he was for thirty years, ever since we were schoolboys. Supposing that he had somehow succeeded in pulling the wool over the public eyes, there might be some argument for a refusal to work with him now. But it is, as you know, just the other way round. It so happens that the misdemeanours both of his private and his public life have received glaring publicity, and every one knows, or thinks that he knows, just what sort of a person Tony is. I cannot see what cause of morality could possibly be served by a refusal to associate with him now. People differ, not nearly so much in what they have done, as in what they have been discovered to have done. "Use every man after his deserts—and who should 'scape whipping?" And, to those who have not 'scaped whipping, however richly they may have deserved it, I feel a kindness, for, "God shall repay; they are safer so." In a way, they are at an advantage over the rest of us, and I only feel confirmed in my kindness when good friends warn me that I shall do myself harm by association with such people. I have little love for those jackals of virtue who live by preying on the corpses of the exposed. They are the least attractive of the animal tribe.

Yours ever, Peter

30

June 17, 1943.

My dear,

I did so enjoy my breath of Somerset, and Margaret and Robert, too. It is, I must confess, a little bit of a relief to come across the young who are not problems, and I am sure that nobody could call either Margaret or Robert a problem. Robert is almost aggressively unproblematical. I never really understood what an extrovert was till I met him. Life to him is refreshingly a question of what to do with something external—a cricket-ball, a cow, the side of a hill, a daffodil—and no questions asked about why they are or whether

> *The grass and the tree*
> *Should continue to be*
> *When there's no one about in the quad,*

or any nonsense like that. And, as for Margaret, I can
never stop saying to myself,

> *And Paul said and Peter said*
> *And all the saints, alive or dead,*
> *Vowed she had the sweetest head*
> *Of yellow, yellow hair.*

How clever it was of you to make them, my dear! They
are so much better than mine, in one respect, at any rate.
They are the last of the pre-machine age and are frightened
of telephones and prefer riding ponies to riding motor-
bicycles and ask if they may put on the wireless occasion-
ally for a treat. I am afraid that mine, on the other hand,
are the first brood of the brave, new world and spend
their noble lives ringing up or being rung up by their
little friends and bawling at them into that little hole for
hours on end. God, how I hate telephones! A ruder instrument was never invented. You are just in the middle
of a conversation and then "*ping*" goes that bloody little
noise, interrupting everything, and without so much as
the shadow of an apology. The only comfort is that the
service is now so bad that I hope that people will give
up using the things and take to walking instead to save
time. I went the other day to Wilde's *Ideal Husband*.
It is a silly play, with a plot full of improbabilities, and I
could not for a time guess why it was so popular both with
me and with the company at large. Then I jumped to it,
of course. It was the inconceivable delight of being trans-
ported back into a society which did not know telephones.
It is my one relic of my adolescent socialism that I still

believe in the nationalisation of the telephone system, because I do think it so frightfully important that telephones shall be as bad as possible.

By a parity of reactionary reasoning, I do hope that petrol rationing is never abolished. If that has come to stay, then I feel that the World War will not have been altogether in vain. I am not against motor-cars absolutely, but it is essential that a ride in them should always remain a treat. When people go seventy miles for lunch, day after day, just for something to do, you have barbarism. You remember that retired banker in Austin, Texas, who drove 200 miles there and back every day of his life to Houston and, when we asked him why, he said that he hated wasting time. But a ride once in a way does no one any harm, and it has the great advantage that you really can cover enough ground to get the contrasts of county with county. It enables you, in a measure, if you do not do it too often, to get what I might call a God's-eye point of view.

I loved those two days driving I had with the children right over all Somerset and beyond, when I saw Mendips and Exmoor and Blackdown all blown to life with one tremendous wind.

> *Dansez, Chantez, villagers! la nuit gagne*
> *Le mont Falcon.*
> *Le vent qui viendra à travers la montagne*
> *Me rendra fou.*

But, with me, rather I have the hope that it will make me sane.

We went down one day through Sedgemoor and

Taunton and out to Brendon and Exmoor and drank cider and ate sandwiches near Whaddon Cross. I am, of course, by adoption and by loyalty, a man of Mendip. It is the home of little men and little arms—none of the great barns, like cathedrals, that you get in Wiltshire—and, by comparison, Exmoor is wild land, the home of the red deer rather than of man.

But I really enjoyed more the next day, where we went further South to the Blackdown Hills—the whole world a blaze of rhododendrons, and then back by the Quantocks and Poldens and through Sedgemoor, as the evening was gathering in, and up Cheddar Gorge at dusk, and so to bed. I wish that you had been there. Everyone can rage about hills, but not so many people have noticed what a strange and attractive and rather terrifying country Sedgemoor is—like Christina Rosetti in the sunshine and a frightening fairyland rising up from beneath the sea when there is a bit of mist about. In the morning

> My heart is like a singing bird
>   Whose nest is in a water'd shoot,
> My heart is like an apple tree
>   Whose boughs are bent with thick-set fruit;
> My heart is like a rainbow shell
>   That paddles in a halcyon sea.
> My heart is gladder than all these
>   Because my love has come to me.

"What love has come to you?" you may say. I do not know. The road to Boroughbridge. Something clicks, and you see things suddenly as they are. That is what

Dante says—not exactly in those words. But, in the gathering evening, Sedgemoor is pure masochistic *frisson*. The black soil and crimson osier give it a sinister colour, as the storms blow up in the sky behind the village churches that stand the highest marks upon the landscapes.

What a wonderful view you get from the ramparts of Shaftesbury, over the Blackmore Vale and villages whose names seem to have been made in fairyland—Buckhorn Western, Stour Provost, Fifehead Magdalen, Purse Candle —Melbury Hill to the south, Winkelbury to the east, and, to the north, one can see past the hills of Fonthill and Knoyle to Pendelwood, where, on a bluff, stands King Alfred's Tower. Beyond that is Maiden Bradley. Do you remember how Maiden Bradley gave Bobby one of his favourite quotations? It comes from William of Malmesbury, I think. There was an argument whether miracles ever happened in the West Country. It was argued out for a number of pages, until it was clinched by the example of the flowering of the Christmas Thorn at Glastonbury— " '*quod expertum est*,' quoth the prior of Maiden Bradley," said old Bill, which, as Bobby used to say, brought an argument to a conclusion about as effectively as it possibly can be brought.

I wish that you had been with us—instead of in Northamptonshire, of all counties. Margaret, of course, is a good substitute, as also is Robert, but both, after all, are only half you, and here two halves do not quite make a whole.

> *But niggard Nature's trick of birth*
> *Bars, lest she enjoy,*

> *Renewal of the loved on earth*
> *Save with alloy.*

Perhaps "alloy" is rather an offensive word, but there are not so many things, after all, that rhyme with "joy," and, anyway, who would ever have thought that one would begin to get sentimental about one's sister? What things we are coming to!

Yours, Peter

31

My dear,

If Robert wants to learn how to plough, I can, at any rate, tell him that. That is just what I do know about farming. I know how to learn things, even if I do not know how to do things, but everything that I have ever learnt about farming was consciously learnt at an age when I was really too old to learn anything. I did not grow into it. But, even to those who grow into things, there must be a day when they do them for the first time.

To begin with, I feel that it is a great sign of grace in him that he even wants to plough with horses. The young these days are all tractor-minded and despise everything that is not internally combusted. But I feel that it is such a short time before either all our food will be produced by atomic energy, or else we shall all be blown up by atomic energy, that we must just as well go on, for the short time left to us, along more old and more gracious ways. And there is a graciousness about horses—a very noble patience in their stupidity. I was looking only yesterday at a reproduction of Gainsborough's "Home from Harvest." You know, there was a carrier who lived in Bath called Wiltshire. He was nuts on painting, and, when he fetched and carried for Gainsborough, he refused ever to take any money, thinking it sufficient honour to work for so great a painter. But he did say that, when he had done enough work to earn a picture, he would be proud if Gainsborough would paint him one. So, in the end, Gainsborough got hold of Wiltshire's horse and cart and put Wiltshire's children on top, dressed all up in blue like farmer boys in a pantomime, and painted the whole caboodle. It is a cheat of a picture in a way, when one learns the whole story, because I do not know that the children had ever done any harvesting in their lives, and, if they had, they certainly never would have done it in those clothes. But, of course, he wanted them in blue, so as to go against the background of the sky. Anyway, it makes rather a pleasant picture, and why should not painters cheat?

I could not help thinking of the contrast between those Wiltshire children and Robert, riding home on a farm-cart. Robert is very neat and well-dressed for a schoolboy when he wants to be, but he once said to me something that I have always thought profoundly true. He said, "Peter, it's only worth while being tidy, if you have something to be tidy from." All life is Withdrawal and Return—and in nothing more than in clothes. With drawal from clothes and return into them. That, surely, is the whole meaning of the phrase "dressing up." "Up" means something special—to a higher level than normal. So I cannot imagine Robert coming back from harvest in his best Sunday clothes. His manners are rather Chaucerian. You remember how Chaucer said what "joy" it was to see people sweat. I quite agree with him, so long as there are not too many of them, and it is in the open air. Chaucer enjoyed people sweating as much as Pepys enjoyed them snoring, and I can follow Chaucer, even if I cannot follow Pepys.

Anyway, what Robert has to do if he wants to plough with horses is this. The first thing that he has to do is to get up very early in the morning and harness the horses himself and go out there alone so that nobody else sees either his glory or his shame. Is that easily done? Then he has to cut two sticks and peel them so that they will show up clearly in the light. Then he must set them up, one in the centre and the other at the far end of the field. Thus, he gets what soldiers used to call "a point to march on." Couple the two horses well apart from one another, so that you can get a clear view of the sticks between them. Then, when you start, do not look either at the horses or at the plough, but keep your eyes firmly fixed on the center stick. Let your arms keep the plough straight.

You must take the horses one on either side of the centre stick. After that, fix your eyes on the far stick and bring the horses to rest exactly by it. If you can do that, you can do everything. It is the first furrow that counts. Any fool can get the rest right, if he has got that right.

I am not sure that my advice to him about milking is quite so valuable. When we bought that heifer just before the war, our experiences—and indeed hers—you remember, were not altogether fortunate. First, she started off by having her calf prematurely, which was in itself an act of inconsideration, and then she had no intention of surrendering her mother's milk to blundering human hands. If there is one thing in the world worse than a dog in a manger, it is a cow in a manger. If her calf could not have that milk, then nobody should have it. Of course, it was quite reasonable that the cow should have its whack, but the little beast had already found its mother's udder and sucked its fill out of it, and the thing still was distended, so really there was no reason why Tom and I should not have come in as second preference shareholders. But the heifer had other views.

Tom wanted me to hold her head, while he attempted to milk her from as safe a distance as possible, but he had not drawn much before a great, back-footed kick sent the pail skimming across the shed. I then tried my hand, with no better result—indeed, with much worse result, for she succeeded in kicking my shins as well as upsetting the bucket. In the end, Tom had to tie her legs together while we were milking, and this had always to be done for some weeks, until maternal passion had a little cooled.

Even after we had returned to habits of less fettered milking, there were several sudden irruptions and the milk was often spilled all over the floor. But, on the whole, we won, and, when the second call came, she made no fuss at all. I remember Tom looking at the pail full of milk and saying, "I feel just as if I had done something myself." I felt like that, too.

Of course, you do all your milking by electricity now, and I daresay that you are quite right. I am not anti-machinery, but I always wonder whether it really works —I mean, in the long run—either with animals or with men. We all know, of course, that it works in the short run—that you can get as much milk out of a given cow with much less trouble. But I always wonder whether there will not be over the generations some deterioration in the breed, as a result of being treated unnaturally—or, at the least, of being treated differently from the way in which their ancestors have been treated ever since time immemorial. It is much like Macbeth, who got the throne all right, but got it in such a way that he would have been better without it. As Stevenson said, "many a man has been ruined by his first murder." Thus, railway trains worked, in the sense that you got to your destination very much more quickly than your ancestors had ever got there. But I should not be surprised if rapid locomotion turned out to be one of the causes of a falling birth-rate in the next generation, and now, when we have telephones, and radios and aeroplanes, every one is manifestly dotty.

A woman came to call on me yesterday, who said that she was the illegitimate daughter of Abraham Lin-

coln and Florence Nightingale and born out of a bottle
and would I lend her half a crown? She had pince-nez
and a snub nose and a curious sort of velvet band round
her neck, and all that I can say was that, if all that she told
me was true, then it did not say much for bottles.

Yours ever, Peter

32

September 9, 1943.

My dear,

How exciting this Italian surrender is, isn't it? And,
for you, all too exciting. I don't want to be a kill-joy. I
very much hope that it means that Martin will be able to
get home, and I hope that it may mean it, but we must
keep our heads, in contradistinction to what some of the
journalists are doing. If we are able to strike at once and
seize all Italy, that will, of course, be grand and will mean
among other things that Martin is free. But it is no good
assuming that all Italy will fall in to us, just because
Badoglio has signed a piece of paper. The Germans will
obviously hang on if they can. It pays them much better
to fight in Calabria than to fight on the Brenner—and they

may be able to—or they may be able to stand on some intermediate line in the middle of Italy somewhere. I certainly do not know—and I don't suppose that anybody knows. But, also, I am afraid that you must make up your mind to it that they will not willingly allow hale and hearty young British officers to get free. Even if they have to go back into the Reich, themselves, they will, if they can, take their prisoners with them.

That is the dark side. The hopeful side is, of course, that, if it is a *sauve qui peut*, they will be mainly concerned to save themselves and may not have time to bother about Martin, and, in any event, in the confusion the chances of escape will be considerably greater than heretofore and, after escape, there are now some Allied lines to escape to We can but wait and see.

Good luck, my dear. You know how much I mind.

Peter

33

My dear,

I have just got your telegram to say that there is news that Martin has got through to Naples. Of course, you know that I simply cannot tell you how delighted I am—for your sake as much as for his—and shall not rest until we hear more news, but, in the meanwhile, must just send you this in great haste to catch the post.

The very best of love,

Peter

34

September 20, 1943.

My dear,

Certainly I will tell you all about Michael Paravane's fair at Hinton Charity. It is one of the oldest in England—the oldest, I think, except that at Axbridge. Of course,

Michael lies about it, and its mediaeval history is all pretty dubious, though it certainly had one, but it has a genuine Elizabethan charter, under which the masters of the fair are constituted a "pie-powder court," with authority to imprison in the stocks all "vagrants, ragamuffins, beggars, gypsies, witches, usurers, or players at football." The only person I ever heard of as being arrested there under the last category was Parsons, Martin's housemaster, who last year tried to punt a cocoanut at the prize pig, just as Mrs. Jenkinson was guessing its weight—an absurd performance.

Why the fête now takes place in Michael's garden, instead of at the Market Cross, I cannot imagine—something to do with the enclosures, I imagine. The fair lapsed for the first few years of the war, but then, last year, when his house was occupied by black troops who kept him awake all night strumming on the banjo, Michael very sensibly said that since they were Negroes, anyhow, and minstrels, anyhow, they might as well be Negro minstrels, and so he made them into a band and, as it were, draped a fête round them. I have always been rather spoiled for fêtes, since I saw the one at San Luis Potosí on the way to Mexico City, but I must say that Michael got quite a decent merry-go-round, which jiggled along to music not more hideous than usual. Its only fault was that it did not have any way to stop and would have been going on still if the air marshal had not deliberately shoved a spanner into its works. Oh, and then there were all the usual things that no one ever can do—shooting ping-pong balls and throwing rings over packets of cigarettes and covering shillings with pennies in a pail of water, and then there was a jumble-stall with a pair of pants, and two left-boots and a bust of Bismarck. One way and another, it was rather a good show.

Certainly you ought to go. Most people hate fêtes because they do not like human beings, but you and I are exceptions. Of course, the villagers all cheat about their exhibits. I must say that it would be much more fun if they did not, but people are so damned competitive these days. The war, which has done so much good in so many ways, has given a great fillip to these local shows. People have to go to them, now that they can't get about in char-a-bancs. I suppose that there is no chance of petrol rationing being reduced, and the ration staying forever. That will be my platform when I stand for Parliament.

I wrote to ask Michael for his evidence about the history of the fête, but he did not answer. Roman Catholics, I find, never do answer letters.

Yours, Peter

35

My dear Ruth,

If Robert wants to know why pie-powder court was so called, I will tell him with the greatest of pleasure. It is a special court established and only having jurisdiction during a fair. Pie-powder is French, corruption of *pied-poudre*—foot-dust. It was so called because justice was done immediately, i.e., while the dust still was on the foot. So now he knows something.

I will tell him something more. At Hinton Charity during harvesting, right up till the time of Michael's grandfather, they all used to stop work for ten minutes at eleven o'clock and have a drink, which was called "beever," a corruption of "*bouvoir*"—the old form of *boire*. Dumplings made out of flour, water and salt were called "swimmers." "Jerusalem artichokes" have nothing to do with Jerusalem. Their real name is "girasole artichokes." That is to say, "artichokes like sunflowers." The Mouros of Foulis have to present the king with a bucket of snow every time that he visits them. And why do you think that the bowler hat is so called? Because the first one was designed by William Bowler of Southwark on the order of the nephew of Coke of Norfolk. And why do you think a booking-office is so called? Because, in the old coaching days, whenever you bought a ticket they wrote your name in a book. And why do people score by fifteens at tennis? Because the French kings betted fifteen louis at a time. Forty should be forty-five! So now, when Robert goes back to school, he will know everything.

God bless the squire and her relations.
And keep them in their proper stations.

Peter

36

October 3, 1943.

My dear,

I just saw Martin for a few minutes, as he will have told you, on his way through London, but, as you will have heard from him all his news much more fully than I at present know it, I will not burden you with it. I am glad that, through everything, he still remains obstinately non-political—almost an "idiot," in the Greek sense of the word. The world needs idiots badly in these stinking ideological days. Maybe he will have political opinions one day, but there is plenty of time for that, and in the meantime he teaches the world a much-needed lesson with his obstinate refusal to regard the Italian who tried to murder him as other than a figure of comedy. "Think of 'em as animals, and they ain't so bad," was the advice that an old Chicago lawyer gave me about the human race. If you don't do that, you sink into Swift's *saeva indignatio,* and this, terrific as it is as literary technique, is in real life itself just a little cracky.

Martin carries on him some of the marks of strain, but, as you know, I am an anti-patholog in such matters. Obviously, there comes a cracking point, a point of nervous breakdown, when one must treat such ailments, but, short of the cracking point, I think that nerves are best conquered by being defied. Pathologists are like armament manufacturers. They largely create the market which they satisfy. They make people nervous by telling them that they are so, and a little haymaking, a few baths, a couple of innings at cricket and a number of pints of beer are, I think, the medicines that he needs for that disease. Let him get—indeed make him get—a little drunk just once or twice. That is what does a man a world of good.

That walking down the centre of Italy is a joke, now that it is all over, but it was not a joke at the time. I was horrified at his legs—like hard, steel ramrods. But, at twenty-two, the body mends. I should not worry too much about that.

Of course, what is so rum for him is the war being still on. Any fool can relax when a war is over, and most fools do. But, supposing that one's own war ends when the general war is still going on—and I hope that Martin's

war has ended? Ought one to relax? How can one help it?
I do not know what he is thinking. I expect that, by
now, you know a great deal better than I do. I know that
he is glad to be home again and back with you, but,
whether that is natural hatred of the boredom of captivity
or whether he has found Barton in Italy,

> *Heard on Lavernia Scargill's whispering trees*
> *And pined by Arno for his lovelier Tees,*

it will be interesting to see. The main experience of his
captivity about which he wanted to talk to me was, oddly
enough, not the food, nor the Italians nor the lavatories,
but that odd nightmare that he has had from time to time
ever since Bobby's death and his schooldays—the nightmare of Bobby walking up this strange street, and that odd
Greek boy, shooting him and then grinning out at him
from behind the barbed wire. Apparently, he had this
dream night after night in prison. It was a sign of the state
that his nerves were in, that he should go on worrying
about it so. Why the dream should have come to him in
the first place I cannot tell, but, at any rate, there is nothing
mysterious now in its recurrence, because he has got himself into such a state that he thinks about it all day and,
therefore, naturally dreams about it all night. But I am
sure that he will be right again soon.

Love, Peter

37

Boxing Day, 1943.

My dear,

I have been thinking over your point about there being apparent contradictions in the Christian scheme, and I should not let it worry you very much. All things go out into mystery, and every system—Catholic, Protestant, atheist, theist, materialist, spiritual—is bound, *apparently*, to contradict itself somewhere or other—God's foreknowledge and free will—if all is matter, how explain the existence of spirit?—if all is spirit, how explain the existence of matter? All these basic dilemmas have puzzled people since the beginning of time and will, obviously, go on puzzling them until its end. But is not the fault with those who talk about Christianity as a solution, who think of it as a sort of book of all the answers? The difficulties are inherent in the very nature of the attempt of a limited intellect to comprehend unlimited reality—to "hold eternity in your hand," as Blake would say.

> *There is no Pilotry my soul relies on*
> *Whereby to catch beneath my bended hand*
> *Faint and beloved along the extreme horizon*
> *That unforgotten land.*

Dean Church, as I think I have remarked before, said,

"Christ did not come to clear up the perplexity, but to show which side to take." Surely, that's the answer.

Yours, Peter

P.S. I once met a man in Birmingham who said, "It does not matter what you believe, so long as you are a regular fellow." I think that he was the stupidest man I ever met.

38

July 19, 1944.

My dear,

I went over to Marlborough to see Martin play cricket the other day. The trouble about Marlborough is the London Road. Most people enter it or leave it that way, and neither in nor out is that way particularly thrilling, but, if you come up from the south from Pewsey and Oare and look down on Marlborough from on top, like looking from the rim on something left at the bottom of a cup, it is quite a different story.

All that country off to the left between Marlborough and Devizes—out towards Bishops Cannings and Allington—had you noticed how very well the architecture suits the country?—as it should—just as one ought, if possible, and as I have often said, to eat and drink things in the places where they are made or grown. This is not a sentimentality. It is a need of the stomach—or the eye. So, here the land falls away from the barrow of Adam's Grave, down to the wide terrace below it, with the long saddleback of the Marlborough Dons in the background, and, over the trees, rises up the tall spire of Bishops Cannings' Church; the cottages, with their curved struts and thatched roofs and oriel windows, are built exactly to suit this long sweep of greensand soil. It is a great lesson on the limitations of planning. You can only plan sensibly if you plan with Nature, even as you can only plan sensibly if you plan with History. You remember John Betjeman's terrible threat of the Planster's Vision:

I have a Vision of the Future, chum.
  The workers' flats in fields of soya beans
  Tower up like silver pencils, score on score;
And Singing Millions hear the Challenge come
  From microphones in communal canteens
  "No Right! No Wrong! All's Perfect Evermore!"

Although Martin only made fourteen, it was obvious that Italian wickets had not spoiled his style, and, if first class cricket gets going again after the war, he ought to be an asset to the Somerset eleven. He was out to a beautiful one-handed catch in the slips off a fast ball outside the off stump, which he ought to have left alone, but which he had a cut at out of sheer *joie de vivre*. An old salt in an

143

I Zingari tie in the pavilion said: "Only a damned good bat would have hit that ball at all. Jessop would have got four off it, but you have to be damned good even to get out to it."

If you want me to tell you what is the matter with Martin, well, my dear, it is obvious. He is pining to get back to the war, or, at least, to get back to the Mediterranean. You may say: "What is the sense of that, when he is not passed fit for active service, anyway? Why can't he be content to be chairborne in the wilds of Hampshire? It's as good a place as any other." Well, people aren't content in a war—that's all there is to it. People in England usually want to get out of England, and people out of England usually want to get back to England. Everybody is intriguing all the time just to be somewhere different— usually not for any particular reason. That is what war is.

Of course, I quite see his wanting to go to Italy. Who would not want to go to Italy in the general way? But the trouble with Italy at the moment is that the Germans have got all the best parts. It is very bad luck on us and very bad luck on the Italians that we have had to enter the country, as an Italian said, "through the kitchen entrance." As you know, I am by no means one of those who think themselves superior persons in the company of all foreigners. On the contrary, my fault is, perhaps, rather to romanticise them—foreigners in general and Italians in particular. But by Italians I mean North Italians —Tuscans and Lombards principally—not "the bloody Piedmontese" and, still less, the even bloodier Venetians. But, with all the will in the world, nobody can really make much of a song-and-dance about the Neapolitans. The great mistake is to think of them as Italians—indeed, as Europeans at all. The Tiber is the frontier of Europe, as Juvenal discovered.

Naples is not a pleasant place to-day, but it is not altogether the fault of the Neapolitans. The town has been knocked about a bit, it is true, but I do not complain of that. On the whole, our bombing there was pretty good and almost all the destruction was in the docks where it was meant to be. There is a whole lot of Naples that ought to have been knocked down and was not. Anyway, it is the non-knocked-down parts that are the worst. Whatever the faults of the Neapolitans, they had a very pleasant café life, father and mother and the children sitting out on the pavement and sipping a glass of *vino*.

It is no improvement to find those Vomero cafés all reserved "for officers only," and full of shouting, bawling, drunken men from Oklahoma, dragging in women off the streets by the scuffs of their necks. Then the men talk about the women in front of their faces as if they were cattle to be appraised—presuming (I suppose, rightly) upon their ignorance of English. You remember what Rochester wrote:

> *She drudges on in tasteless vice*
> *As if she sinned for exercise.*

It is more true of the men than the women here, but, either way round, nothing is less attractive than sin without romance, justified solely on arguments of hygiene. The women will do anything, because they are starving—

maybe they would do anything anyway—but, at least, that is the reason given. The rations are worse than they were under the Germans. But such a regimen does not make either the Americans, or, to a lesser extent, us, popular with the Neapolitan young men.

I was having lunch in a black market restaurant, the Imperiale, just under that arch off the Via Roma, and a priest without any shoes on came in begging. There was a drunken American sergeant at the next table, who alleged that he was an ex-seminarian. He started doing a ribald parody of the Mass—all the words and all the gestures—and the other soldiers all laughing at him. Can you imagine anything more horrible? It was the only time for years and years that I have ever lost my temper and hit somebody. When I did hit him, I must confess that he had the grace to apologise. "You're quite right, boss," he said, "I ought to be ashamed of myself"—which was something.

And then I remember the blueness of the sky and the blueness of the sea and the sun and the curve of the coast line, and even—to give man a little bit of credit—the lights blinking out to sea at night-time, and the memory of a thunder-storm, and I long to be back there, in spite of it all.

I stood at Naples once, a night so dark
I could have scarce conjectured there was earth
Anywhere, sky or sea or world at all;
But the night's black was burst through by a blaze—
Thunder struck blow on blow, earth groaned and bore
Through her whole length of mountain visible;

There lay the city thick and plain with spires,
And, like a ghost disshrouded, white the sea!

So I do sympathise with Martin's desire to get back
to the Mediterranean, and I do sympathise with his ambition to have as good a war record as possible—the more
so, after he has been told that he is not physically fit.
There is nothing heroic about this, there is nothing particularly patriotic. It is simply an expression of the enormous pleasure in physical achievement, and revulsion
from themselves when they fail of achievement, which
most healthy people have. I went last night to dine at the
barracks, and after dinner they wanted me to play splosh;
you know, I rather disapprove of those games on a billiard
table. It is like playing baseball on a cricket ground, or
spitting in church. Billiard tables were made for billiards,
not for people who were too lazy to learn how to play
billiards to hit balls about on. But, if I had to play, I was
mad keen to play well. I do not mean to win. I do not
much mind about winning, one way or the other—but I
do loathe aiming at a ball and missing it. I would sooner
be dead, and I wished to God that I had not had two pink
gins before dinner. Not that I was in the least bit tiddly,
but you have got to be absolutely clear, if you are going
to hit balls straight. Well, Martin feels just like that about
doing well in the war.

I know that that will make you angry, and you will
say, "If he can't see any more in the war than that, it is
very immoral for him to fight in it!" Women, if you will
forgive the phrase, do say that. They are more directly

rational than men—want to go straight to a point, but, the more I see of life, the more wrapped round with mystery I find it, the more futile seem to me these presumptuous attempts to regulate one's conduct, on the pretence that one can possibly understand the general plan or estimate the general good. And the more I approve of people who act for confessedly limited motives. I hate people who think that they are God. Pardon me, Mrs. Fosset.

Love, Peter

39

October, I forget what, 1944.

My dear,

Caserta in summer is like an oven, and everybody loathes it. The Kings of Naples built it to be like Versailles, but it is the *reductio ad absurdum* when people neglect climate in architecture and try and build what suits one latitude in another—like Byzantine architecture in England or those absurd pseudo-Greek State capitols in America. I was glad to get away, as is everybody, and Sicily was lovely at the wrong time of year (of course, I don't mind heat, so long as I can bathe—most people

148

hate it). The war has now quite passed Sicily by, leaving behind only a lot of soldiers with absolutely nothing to do. It is not good for them. It does no one any great harm to fight in a war, but it does most people a great deal of harm to be behind a war. The curious situation in Italy now is that there is a great deal of grumbling that since D-Day the Italian has become a second-class front, that all the stuff now goes to France, that no one imagines that the war is going to be won or lost in Italy, that, nevertheless, a lot of poor devils have to be killed there—and all that is, I daresay, true. But the odd thing is that you do not get very much of that talk on the battle-front, but, the farther from the front, the more of it there is—until, in Sicily, it ranks second only to bawdy as a staple topic of conversation.

Well, then, now I've come across to here—the Albergo del Mehari in Tripoli. Of course, it's just a hop before lunch in an aeroplane these days, and, therefore, it seems natural enough that the politics of the one coast should be intermingled with the politics of the other coast, but what is so extraordinary is that they should have been just as much intermingled two thousand years ago, when it took months to cross the Mediterranean. One would have thought that there would have been room for both Rome and Carthage in the Mediterranean at that date, but the world was a very small place, even then.

The Albergo del Mehari is an astonishing, Jules Verne-like place. There is an incidental advantage in most absurdities. There was, of course, no real reason why there should be a whacking great hotel in Tripoli at all.

Why should anyone want to stay in Tripoli? But Musso-lini insisted that a hotel should be built there just to show off. I think that the Italians have been, on the whole, the best of modern architects, even though their architecture has often been ridiculous because it has been expended on such unworthy objects. Anyway, the Albergo del Mehari is very good as a hotel, supposing that anybody had wanted a hotel there—the rooms round an open Turkish court-yard, with fountains playing onto the grass—just like illustrations of Omar Khayyám—the sort of place where Jamshyd gloried and drank deep, at the time when Jam-shyd did glory and did drink deep back in the old pre-lion and pre-lizard days, and then, from the central hall, one goes down a lot of steps under the sea and walks along a corridor, full of a lot of fish swimming about, to have lunch in the sort of room where Arsène Lupin used to hide. from the police, but in the middle of the sea and at the bottom of it, or, at least, as near the bottom as makes no difference. That is how we fight the war in Tripoli.

I sat at lunch next to a Hollywood film man, mostly deaf, who went about with a contraption over his ears that looked like a rat-catching machine. He was an able fellow, usually drunk. He was very able at his job, and his work did not suffer in the least, even when he was sober. He was very annoyed, because he had been held up for a week in Algiers, and this had made him miss the liberation of Athens, which he was very anxious to "shoot." It was, he said, "a dirty limey trick" to take Athens before the cameras were ready. The operation, he seemed to think, should have been postponed until the movie men could get there, but then, he comforted himself: "After all, these European capitals are all much the same. When you've seen one, you've seen them all." After lunch we went to the air booking people, so that he could discover where else he could go, instead, now that Athens was no longer "news."

"Can you get me through to Bucharest?" he asked.

"Did you say Bucharest, sir, or Budapest?" they replied.

"Hell, what can it matter?" he answered, "I want to go places."

"Tell me," he said, as we came away, "who does this belong to? Is it part of England?"

But I, too, am sorry not to have been in on the liberation of Athens, though for quite a different reason from that of my Hollywood friend. Suddenly, out of all the morass of boredom and sordidness of this Mediterranean War, there flares up "the light that never was on sea or land"—an appeal of pure romance out of the world of the Crusades or the Song of Roland—the appeal to go in and rescue the people to whom we owe all the glory which our life has ever held, and the country which, to any decent man, is the country which he loves best after his own. It gives us all a cause, and one needs a cause to be happy —that profound paradox of the dissatisfaction with the purely self-regarding. I have not met anyone, anywhere in the Mediterranean, who would not give his eyes to be turning his back on all the world and to be going into Greece. People quite innocent of any classical education have been swept off their feet by the excitement. "There's only one thing wrong about the Greeks," said a tough American major. "There aren't nearly enough of them." "Of course, one gorges in Cairo and starves in Athens," said a charming young South African transport command pilot, "but then who would not rather starve in Athens than gorge in Cairo?"

And, as for us, who have been soaked in Herodotus and Hellenic Travellers' Cruises and all that, it is so exciting that I can hardly bear to sit down. Don't you remember that old Abbot in Chios who gave us bread and honey and took us up the tower from which they drove off the Turks, so that we could see the view—the grey of the olive trees and, beyond that, the green of the pines, and then the white of the city and, in the distance, the sapphire blue of the Aegaean, all sparkling in the sun. I always feel like the Negroes who used to sing: "Glory be! Glory be! Lord, he send us the sun." Or, again, do you remember drinking nasty resinated wine in a police post, while the waters of the Gulf of Corinth were lazily piling themselves up in little ripples on the shells of the shore, or the first fall of snow on Hymettus, and the purple crocuses peeping up through it, and the sentry, sitting in his little hut, drinking and staring into the crackling pine-wood fire? All that is rising from the dead. Don't you feel just mad with excitement?

Yours, Peter

40

My dear,

I got back to England yesterday—breakfast in Naples
and an early tea in Lyneham—not bad going. I was in the
club by dinner-time and found David, with his wife, in
the ladies' annex. At least, I think that it was his wife,
but, really, he has so many lady-friends and is so charming and intimate with them all, with his "my dears" and
"darlings," that I find it a little difficult to remember
which of them are his wives and which of them are not.
However, he told me that Martin had gone into Greece.
I thought that he very likely would have done so, ever
since I had seen him going round Bari, with a notice on
him to say that he was a spy, and every day driving to and
fro to an absurd place called Monopoli, where the most
disreputable eggs are hatched. The lucky devil!

And then this morning I had a letter from him, all
about his journey in—I suppose that you have had it all,
too. I can smell every inch of that journey—the tough
Greek naval officers stamping to and fro across the plane
and arguing with one another.

"There's Hydra."

"No, it isn't; it's Spetsai."

"That's the Gulf of Corinth."

"Of course, it isn't. There's much more land than that between Argos and the Gulf of Corinth."

"It's the Gulf of Aegina, not the Gulf of Corinth."

Then, the moment when at last they saw Sunium to their right and Salamis at their feet and, with a triumphant "There she is, there she is," the Parthenon, serene, superb, untouched. It must have given them the feeling that the hosts of hell had done their worst and had prevailed nothing against the beauty of Athens on a lovely October morning.

And then the drive in from Kalamai—such a typical commentary on this strange modern world, that the air should be full of aeroplanes, but the land so denuded of vehicles that it should take longer to get from Kalamai to Athens than from Ban to Kalamai, and longer than it would have taken Socrates to walk, 2200 years ago. I am glad that Martin was well kissed, alike by male and female, washed and unwashed. It must be so wonderful to be in a place where it is the British who are popular —not the Allies, and not the Americans and not the Russians. This is our show, our one show, our very own show, and I hope to heaven that we make a good go of it. I was, of course, amused in a way at his tale of the two people firing off guns at one another at the very time that they were both cheering the British, but all such stories, even if they have their funny side, are also very tragic. I do hope that it will prove that the discipline of suffering has really made a unity of the Greeks at last, and they will be able to transcend their absurd party politics. It will be such a triumph for the Greeks if they can, and such a proper commentary on Hitler, if his one constructive contribution to European politics should prove to be that he has brought unity to the Greeks—unity through their hatred of him. I have hopes. The Greeks have a longer tradition than any other people to teach them that there is a glory and a discipline in suffering. You remember what Hecuba said:

> *Had He not turned us in His hand, and thrust*
> *Our high things low and shook our hills to dust,*
> *We had not been this splendour, and our wrong*
> *An everlasting music for the song*
> *Of earth and heaven.*

That is the great question. Will they prove "this splendour," prove capable of accepting suffering as a glory and a discipline? I hope so, and, if so, it will be the greatest triumph of history. But there is a breaking point beyond which suffering is not acceptable.

Love, Peter

41

My dear,

The trouble with Margaret's speculations about progress is that there is no mathematical way of measuring the progress of one age over that of another, or the happiness of one person against the happiness of another. But, in so far as there is evidence, I should have honestly thought that most of it was against Margaret.

The two best measures of progress, imperfect as they are, seem to be art and food. The art of an age—particularly if you include its popular and peasant art—is a good index how far people find life worth living. By that test one would not call the present age a very happy one. It produces comparatively little art, and what there is of it is not very happy. Another of its peculiarities is that, in spite of social equalitarianism, there is a far wider gulf than there has ever been before between the producers of art and the man in the street. In painting, music, sculpture, poetry, you get this deliberate cult of the grotesque and the ugly. What is the explanation of it? I think that it is satanic—I do not mean in the sense that they have consciously sold their souls for two and six pence with a toad, a pentagram and a strangled hen, but that they deny a purpose and a pattern in life and are in revolt against anyone who professes to see such a purpose and such a pattern there. Well, whatever you may call a world in which such people are on the increase, it is surely violence to language to call it a progressive world. Your case that the world is getting better is a somewhat weak one, if the only evidence that you can produce is that there is an increase in the number of disillusioned men and women who say that it is getting worse. If you must have girls, make them read Dostoievsky. He knew all the answers to these questions.

The other test is food. The vaguer "standard of living" is much less satisfactory, because standard of living includes all sorts of rackety things like cinemas and telephones and radios and motor-cars and high explosives, of which it is the very question in dispute whether people are the happier for having them. But what is the evidence given by food? Quite apart from the abnormalities of the war, it is by no means as happy a one as Margaret seems to think. Sir John Orr, who is the best expert going on this, tells us that a quarter of our people are undernourished—in peacetime. (In England by an odd paradox people are, on the whole, better nourished when there is a war on. As opposed to Germany, where they had to choose between guns and butter, in England a lot of people only get butter when they are either making or using guns.) Now, you may say that things are rather better than they were seventy years ago, and so they are, even though much of the food, if less abundant, is of poorer quality than it used to be. Most modern inventions in packing, freezing, dehydrating, etc., have been inventions of ways of making worse food just stay on the stomach and of turning quick poisons into slow ones. But has your good daughter ever read the works of Thorold Rogers? If not, she ought to. Thorold Rogers was a very interesting and a very important man and, I believe, reliable. He took the figures of the ruling wages and the ruling prices at different dates throughout the four hundred years pervious to his writing, and calculated how many weeks' work would have been required for an agricultural labourer to earn subsistence for himself and his family. At every date which he took between 1470 and 1870, the standard of living by this test was found to have fallen, with the result that in 1870 the agricultural labourer was about six times as badly off as he had been in Henry VII's reign. It is true that things have taken a turn for the better since then, if only in that, having fewer agricultural labourers, we pay those that we have got a good deal better. But there it is. The common notion that things have been steadily getting rather better through the ages is quite untrue.

We had quite an amusing lunch when I took Margaret to David's on Tuesday. David gave us half a lettuce each for lunch and spent all the time boasting what an enormous dinner he had at night. I suppose that such things must be in wartime, but, as Dr. Johnson said, it was "not a meal to ask a man to."

Love, Peter

42

My dear,

I had a very interesting letter from Martin, who seems to be enjoying himself very much in Greece, even though the food situation is very bad and the political situation none too good—"something political, I suppose," as our driver in Mexico said, when we saw that woman come up and stab a policeman at Guadaloupe. But his account of his visit to, and the view from, the Acropolis did make my mouth water, I must say. You remember Byron:

> *Slow sinks, more lovely, as his race be run*
> *Along Morea's hills the setting sun,*
> *Not as in northern climes obscurely bright*
> *But one unclouded mass of living light.*

Martin asks why Byron has nothing at all to say about the modern city of Athens. I have written and told him the answer, which is, briefly, that there was no modern city of Athens in Byron's time. Ancient Athens perished completely in the second century A.D. It virtually ceased to exist from the time of Pausanias until it reappeared as a small Turkish village in the seventeenth century. In Byron's time it had a population of, perhaps, 20,000. All the inhabited part of Athens is a completely boring modern city. The part up to Lycabettus, you remember, was not even built when we went there as children before the last war.

Martin tells me that he could see Acro-Corinth from Athens. One forgets how small a country Greece is. I have seen the Acropolis and, indeed, even the Royal Palace and right out beyond as far as Sunium from the Height of Acro-Corinth. What a wonderful thing it would be if only they would set up the organisation of the new United Nations in Athens! It is just the right place for killing war. You remember that it was in the Areopagus that Ares—War—was tried for the murder of Halirrhothius, and, of course, it was there that Athena proclaimed the doctrine of mercy that brought the Oresteian blood feud to an end.

> The King,
> *Treading the purple calmly to his death,*
> *While round him like the clouds of eve, all dusk*
> *The giant shades of fate, silently flitting,*
> *Pile the dim outline of the coming doom.*

And then comes Athena to say that, if blood must always have blood, the feud will go on until the end of time. Therefore, why not stop now? "Let mercy prevail." Is not that just the place where the foundation stone of the modern world should be laid?

Did Martin tell you of the old man who came up to him and said: "God bless England. People will never forget what England has done—either in Greece or in other countries."

"Not even in Germany?" asked Martin—I can't think why.

"Not even in Germany," said the old man.

He says that it is so wonderful to be part of an occupying army that likes the inhabitants of the country which it is occupying—an almost unique achievement. He heard some soldier in a shop in Stadion Street telling the shopkeeper that he ought to charge more for his wares.

I hear that Martin went up to Vathy on the Euripos, opposite Euboea. Vathy, you know, is the old Aulis, from which the Greeks, all of them except poor Iphigenia, sailed to Troy. But, obviously, they could not have done so. It is two tiny pebbly little bays, and, even allowing for the Greek habit of pulling all their boats up on the beach and then launching them one by one, Aulis could no more have launched a thousand ships than could Helen's face. I always rather hate Vathy, because it is the one place in the world that has given me a terrible fear that, perhaps, there is some sense in the rot that the higher critics talk.

When they think of Greece, people think of Athens. But, counting out Athens and a few more show places—Delphi, Olympia, and Mycenae—perhaps the most striking thing about Greece is the extraordinary sordidness and lack of distinction of places that have been magic names to one since one's school-days. I remember very well driving down the pot-holed, grubby central street of a down-at-heels village, dodging a couple of pigs and a boy on a bicycle with the stump of a cigarette sticking out of the side of his mouth—and no industry, except for barbers, who made a living by shaving off one another's moustaches. And then I asked one of these barbers what was the name of the village, and he said "Thebes" (Thivae). It is much the same at Vathy, except that there is not even anybody to ask there—just the ruins of an old fort, which cannot answer back.

Love, Peter

43

November 7, 1944.

My dear,

I had a letter from Robert's tutor yesterday, and he sent me a parody which Robert had written of Sir Henry Newbolt. I thought it rather good and, at any rate, interesting. This is it:

> *My son, the world is almost round*
> > *Your father always found it so.*
> *He used to go by Underground*
> > *The omnibus was far too slow.*
> *You, too, have come to be a man*
> > *And Nelson's best loved liquor pours*
> *From out that simple watering can,*

Stand up and take it—it is yours.
It is not that he drank the stuff,
 His ways were nobler ways than these,
Rather, he left behind enough
 To fill the seven circling seas.
And Drake, who sailed the Spanish Main
 And went the way you, too, must go,
He cried, "Don't bring me that again,"
 And poured it into Plymouth Hoe.

And so it goes on. Why wouldn't it?

The reason why it is interesting is this: Boys like Robert really like Sir Henry Newbolt better than anybody. "A bumping pitch and a blinding light" and "ten to make and the match to win" and "play up, play up, and play the game" is just what unsophisticated young men of fifteen or sixteen, with good eyes and good physique and boundless energy, do really in their heart of hearts like. But, on the other hand, they do not like being laughed at, and they know just enough to know that some people do laugh at that sort of thing. So, the way that they get round it is to parody it. That gives them the excuse for reading it, and, if laughed at, they can pretend that they were laughing, too. But, you may say, the danger is that in time he will come really to laugh at Newbolt and to laugh at himself and to be a general cynic. A danger, of course, but in his case, I think, not a very real one. Real physical excellence, such as Robert has—not merely being good at games, but a true grace in all physical accomplishments—is so rare a possession, so exquisite a pleasure, that there is no fear that he will abandon it for any of the lesser, paler pleasures of the mind. He will be one of those happy people who will never grow up, and for whom life will be "always afternoon." (Do you know why "noon" is called "noon," by the way? I will tell you some time.) The real problems of life for Robert will begin when he is seventy-two and cannot any longer sit on a horse, but all that is some time ahead,—unless, of course, he should get crippled young, but we need not be morbid enough to speculate about that, even in such days as this.

Love, Peter

44

November 10, 1944.

My dear,

Tell Margaret to put a sock in it, and not to be so rude to her uncle. Of course, "noon" is "nones." Any fool —even any uncle—knows that. But why is twelve o'clock called the ninth hour? Can she tell me that? I bet she can't.

They started counting from 6:00 A.M., and, therefore, noon ought to be 3:00 P.M. So it used to be. Now, in Lent, the monks were only allowed one meal a day, and that was the "after-noon" meal. Then, as they got hungrier and hungrier, they pushed "nones" earlier and earlier, "anticipating," as they called it, until St. Dunstan, when he was Abbot of Glastonbury, thought of killing two birds with one stone and having sext and nones all together at 12 o'clock, so that then the monks could lunch at half-past twelve. And everybody thought that that was such a good idea they made him a saint—all except the devil, who tried to interfere and got his nose tweaked with a pair of tongs. But the "afternoon" really ought to be called the "aftersext." I bet that Margaret never knew a word of that, so what the devil is she laughing at?

Yours ever, Peter

45

November 23, 1944.

My dear,

I am interested in what Martin tells me about the Russian colonel in the Meteoron monastery—partly because I am interested in Russian colonels and partly because I am interested in Meteoron monasteries. That the lady who is living with him is an *ersatz* wife, sent to spy on him, and that his real wife is kept on ice in Russia, ready to be toasted, if the Colonel should put a foot wrong, seems to me entirely probable. That is just what they do, and Greece is a tricky country for Communists now, because most of the Communists there are Trotzkyites and anti-Stalin. I am not particularly anti-Russian, but all the truths about the Russians seem to me exactly opposite to what both their friends and their enemies pretend. When any Englishman comes face to face with them, the great difficulty that he finds about getting on with them is that class divisions among them are so much deeper than Western opinion will tolerate. I remember, at an official reception in Persia, one of the waiters called a Russian captain "Comrade." The captain cut him across the face with a riding whip and opened a great gash across his cheek. " 'Captain,' " he said, "to you, and not 'comrade.' " Communism—the opposite to Mussolini's fascism in the famous phrase—is for export and nothing else. In this crumbling world, there is one country, at any rate, which is safe against Communism, and that is Russia. I am not surprised that, as Martin tells me, the colonel was horrified to find that in the British Army "officers did not get even thirty times as much as their men." I believe that Max Eastman's figures are quite reliable, and that the differences in income in Russia are far greater than those in any other country. But I do not so much mind that, myself. It is the differences in social standing that I mind.

As for the monasteries of Meteoron, it was there, you know, that Uncle Dotty landed up one day in Lent at the end of the last century. They said that they would take him in, but they could not give him any supper, because it was Lent and they were fasting. Nor would he have got any if it had not so happened that he had gone to wash his hands. As soon as they saw him pouring water over his hands, a cry went up that he had not been baptised, and the abbot, hearing of the phenomenon, said: "He's an idolater is he? Give him a boiled egg."

The monasteries of the Meteoron—that is to say, the monasteries up in the air—are in Thessaly, near the railhead at Kalabaka. They are perched on the top of curious pillar-like rocks, which rise up, sheer and grey, out of almost luxuriant vegetation. They date from the fourteenth century. At one time there were twenty-four of them, but now there are only five. You go up to them in a cage. I cannot quite make out what either Martin or the Russian colonel was doing there, but, then, I suppose that one is not meant to make out things during the war. Martin seems a trifle more optimistic about Greek politics—I hope justly. The trouble with the Greeks is that they all have violent political opinions, and their opinions vary from day to day, retaining as a constant only their violence. The same man is at the extreme left to-day and at the extreme right to-morrow, consistent only in his extremity. It makes them a very difficult people out of which to form a moderate centre party.

Love, Peter

46

My dear,

What rum things animals are! If you are a Christian,
then they are, it always seems to me, one of the deepest
of all mysteries. We are told that this world only makes
sense—for men—because it is a testing-place. We suffer
here, but it is a discipline, and we shall be recompensed
for our suffering. But, if so, and if, as we are also told,
the animals have not got souls and are not being tested,
how does the world make sense for them? All this creation, pain, suffering, death—for what? We are told that
animals are made to serve man, but what proportion of
animals ever meet a man in all their lives?

But it is another rumness about them that strikes me
most, at the moment. Take that absurd old hen of yours.
For a month she scratched indefatigably in the earth for
her young and never touched a morsel of food till they
had all been fed, picking it up in her beak and dropping
it at their feet. Then, yesterday, she turned on them. I
found that she had trapped one inside the coop, where it
tried to squeeze, but got stuck through being too fat, and
the old hen, until yesterday all red in beak and claw, becomes suddenly once more the friend of man. Guessing
her needs, I pick her up and carry her into the field,
whence she came, and put her down in front of the hen

house, which she had not entered for two months. She walks straight up the plank into a nest box, sees a broody hen, sits down on top of her, and lays an egg.

Now, what does all this prove? Surely, how sensibly hens behave—not attractively, perhaps, but with unsentimental, cold-blooded reason, according to the sort of code that a government of Fabians would attempt to impose upon human beings, but against which human nature would react as too bloodlessly logical. As long as the children need the mother, the mother gives up everything to them! As soon as they can stand on their own legs, *instanter* she turns from them and gives herself to the production of a new family. What could be more sensible, more Benthamite, more plainly conducive to the greater happiness of the greater number?

Then, contrast this utterly reasonable behaviour of birds and beasts without reason with man, who possesses reason, and yet behaves in a manner that is utterly unreasonable. We talk of the law of the jungle, when men kill one another for causes of which none of them could give a coherent account. But the law of the jungle is just what it is not, for animals do not kill one another, except for food or in self-defence. We talk of a man making a beast of himself when he gets drunk. But man is the only beast who ever makes a beast of himself. The animals are all teetotallers. The more I think of it, the more does it seem to me that men are neither selfish nor unselfish, but just plain dotty. If they were merely greedy, they would see that there would be far more for everybody, if they stopped quarrelling and all turned to producing. If they were merely selfish, they would see that it was to everyone's advantage to behave with that minimum of decency, that is necessary to keep the pot boiling. Or, on the other hand, if they liked war, then I suppose that they would have war, with no fuss about it, as one has a football match. Yet they do none of these things. They hate war, yet they must have war. The motives that lead them to war are really sub-selfish, yet they must invent for themselves super-selfish reasons for fighting. Then, having invented them, they forget them. They are greedy, yet they must destroy one another's wealth and destroy their own wealth, in the insane hope that they will get more out of the cake, if only they begin by destroying half of it. Man, with reason, behaves far less rationally than the animals without it—that is the paradox. I remember a chap in the trenches in the last war, when we had a plague of rats. "Rats," he said, "will outlive men. Rats is more rational than men. Men think about no end of things, but rats only think about rats." It was as good a definition of rationalism as another.

Love, Peter

47

Ruth dear,

So the balloon is up in Athens. Oh, my dear, I am so sorry for you. In general I mind terribly, of course—far more, I think, than I have minded anything in this war. It seems like the knell of the last hope of the reign of reason. If this happens in Athens, what is going to happen everywhere? And I hate the people in England who take sides about it, whichever side they take, supporting their fiddling little right-wings and left-wings. As if anyone out of Bedlam cared about these meaningless catchphrases or wished to sit in judgment on individuals in face of the monumental tragedy that it should have happened at all! You know, when Julian the Apostate, at his last throw to restore the old pagan gods, sent to consult the oracle at Delphi on his chances, the oracle said: "Go, tell the emperor that the carved work of the sanctuary is cast down upon the ground, and the God thereof hath no longer where to lay his head. And the laurel of his divination is withered, and the waters that spoke with voices are dried up." And then the oracle shut up shop. The pale Galilean had conquered. It is one of the most moving stories of history, but I feel to-day that the waters that spoke with voices are dried up once more, but dried up, this time, not for something better than good paganism, but for something enormously worse—for the rule of babble and the rule of chaos and the rule of hate.

And, in all that horror, what can I say? You will not misunderstand me, darling. It is your sovereign virtue that you do not misunderstand things, that you allow me to say things to you, however unconventional, so long as they are sincere, and that you find feeling in what is apparently most unfeeling. But it is almost a comfort in all that horror to have an anxiety that is a good anxiety, to know that in all that witches' cauldron of hatred and mad ambition, of the promise of Utopia through the actuality of hell, there is something as solid and as sensible as a mother who is anxious for the safety of her son. It is the nearest that we can come to joy, in such days as these, to find someone who is sorrowing for something sane. Is it unfeeling of me if I say that?

But you know very well, my dear, that, however I may philosophise, and however foolishly I may philosophise, I am not unfeeling about your sorrows. They are never far from my mind, and it would be foolish to pretend that any accident is not possible in such fighting as that now going on in Athens. But do not be too anxious. Fighting of this sort is hateful beyond words. I cannot imagine why, if our Government was going to take a stand, they did not have sufficient troops there to hold things in the first place and to keep it down to the level of a police action. They say that the troops were not available, but that answer is silly. If the troops really were not available, then we should have washed our hands of the whole country and not gone in there at all. As it is, we shall have to send in troops in the last instance, and we might just as well have sent them in in the first instance. I do not think that you need be very seriously alarmed about the immediate, military danger. Fighting the E.L.A.S. is not like fighting the Germans. Even if the E.L.A.S. does seem to hold the Piraeus for the moment, I have no doubt that the British reinforcements will get in soon and relieve the defenders, and, in the meanwhile, casualties can hardly be very heavy among those who stick within the British lines and keep their heads. After all, what can the E.L.A.S. inflict casualties with? They have not got any artillery worth talking about. They have not got any aeroplanes. So don't worry too much, my dear. Nevertheless, no one could long more than I do for this hateful business to be over. But, even then, God knows what will happen. I had hoped that their suffering might have created "this splendour," a living, united, single Greek nation. Papandreou, with all his pedantry and all his faults, has a real belief in legal government and in *concordia ordinum*. He is almost the only man in the Balkan Peninsula who has. Well, the effect of all this must inevitably be to drive out reconcilers like Papandreou and to put into power toughs and "shooting men" who believe in ruling by destroying their opponents. I do not prophesy whether these toughs will be of the left or of the right, nor do I think that that very much matters. What does matter is that the dream, the "everlasting music," the hope of the rule of law is gone.

Oh, my dear, do not ever let us believe that things will go right again in this world. Only then shall we not be disappointed. Only then can we face it.

Love, Peter

48

January 13, 1945.

My dear Ruth,

I have had a long set-to with Martin over the week-end and will sit down now to tell you at some length what I make of him—the more so, as I understand that there were some parts of the story which he felt embarrassed in telling to you. Though I have not the advantage of being your son, I have the advantage of having known you quite literally all my life and of having grown up with you, and I can, therefore, perhaps without indelicacy, say things which even a son cannot say.

Undoubtedly, this Greek business has been a shock to the boy, and he is entirely upset by it. As far as hardship and danger go, he is light-heartedly tough. He had been in far greater danger in battle in Africa and had suffered far more hardship in the Italian prison-camp.

Those are not the troubles. The trouble is the blow to his beliefs.

Up till now his attitude towards life had been that of what I may call "the light-hearted Christian." That is to say, he had taken little interest in politics or the causes of wars, had had a genial contempt for all merely secular faiths and theories of perfectibility and had faced the world with an easy-going charity based upon a firm belief in original sin. He expected everybody to be fairly weak and fairly bad and was not at all put out when his expectations were justified. He was always loud to uphold the moral law in theory, and equally loud to condemn those who were shocked at discovering that anybody had violated it in practice. It was a pleasant enough philosophy of life, as far as it went. The only criticism of it from the orthodox Christian standpoint was one that I once heard Michael Paravane make. "Christians," he said, "are supposed not only to believe in sin, but also to think it horrible. You seem to believe in it, but to find it all frightfully jolly." Broad-mindness is, doubtless, a virtue, but one ought to be a little bit shocked at some things. Martin was not even shocked at an Italian warder trying to knife him.

So, he remained in this spiritually unfledged condition through Oxford and Africa and Italy, but with Greece came a change. He fell a victim to that strange disease to which romantic young Englishmen are so oddly liable. All foreigners are like Dr. Johnson's Irishman. "They never speak well of one another." No foreigner has ever been known to like another foreigner. But Englishmen have a curious habit of falling in love with foreign countries of which they know very little. In obedience to this habit Martin fell in love with Greece, wanted to champion all Greeks and then, with a bump, discovered that it was impossible, as half the Greeks would on no inducement speak well of the other half.

That was the great disillusion, but worse was to come —a particular story—and it is this story which I am anxious that you should understand. I do not know how much of it he has told you, but, as I know that he has not told all, I set it all down now.

You remember that odd young Greek ragamuffin, Eleutheros Corizis, with whom Martin was at school. I met him once or twice, and I think that you did, too. Well, out in Greece, Martin discovered that this young man was now one of the leaders, and one of the most bloodthirsty of the leaders of the E.L.A.S. forces. When the Germans had come into Greece, this young Corizis had gone up into the mountains in Phokis and raised a guerrilla band, which fought a bit against them during the early period of the occupation. Then, after a time, he got tired of fighting Germans and doubtless found life on the Phokian mountain side a trifle lacking in amenities. So, he turned more or less open brigand and preyed on the geese and chickens of the neighbouring peasantry and killed quite a number of the peasants themselves as well.

The taste for the life seemed to grow on him. Having at first killed to live, he in the end lived to kill. He became some sort of ultra-Trotskyite, Bakuninite, nihilist, and evolved a theory that the old order must be destroyed and a new order must be built. In order to destroy and to rebuild, blood had to be shed—not as a regrettable necessity, but as a thing good in itself. While Ares was ruling by murder in the Peloponnese, Corizis set up his headquarters on Mount Lycorea—the classical Parnassus (how appropriate)—and terrorised from there.

There was another chap who had been at school with Martin and this Corizis, whom Martin had knocked up against in Athens. Philsby, I think his name was. He was a doctor—R.A.M.C. One day, word came that a little band of pro-Government Greeks were holding out in a house in Pindar Street at the foot of Mount Lycabettus. Could a doctor go to them? It was agreed that this Philsby should go, and Martin said that he would accompany him. It was not a very military thing to do, but, as Martin's batman put it, "If everybody had stuck to the rules, we could never have had a war at all." So they plastered the ambulance all over with red crosses—"not that I imagine they will do much good," as Philsby said—and set off.

As far as the Ministry of War, all was quiet. They even got a half-hearted cheer and wave from curious hooligans, half corner boys and half troops, who were standing at a somewhat lounging attention outside the Ministry. Then they turned off the Boulevard de l'Académie up Pindar Street.

Martin could see Mount Lycabettus, standing up at the end of the road, and on its summit the little chapel of St. George. On the left-hand side of the street most of the houses were in ruins—blown up by the one side or the other in the fighting. The house at the top of the street, which the Government troops were holding, alone stood intact, surrounded and defended by barbed wire. Suddenly, Martin knew with a sickening horror that this was the street that he used to see in his nightmare—the street up which Bobby used to walk to be murdered by young Corizis. He knew, without looking to see, that there must also be the only other feature of that dream—the gap in the houses beyond the furthest rim, the stone steps, the garden gate, the little, low stone wall, and, behind it, lurking something obscene.

"Look," he began to cry out, not knowing what he was going to say. Before he had time to say anything, a volley of shots rang out. One pierced the engine and put it out of action. The driver and the orderly were both killed. A splinter flew up off the woodwork, and Philsby stood up with his hand on his bleeding face. He started to turn round, and then another shot rang out, and he fell down dead.

There was an answering volley from the defending troops. In the confusion Martin was able to dodge round, so as to get the ambulance between him and the attackers, and then, taking advantage of the confusion of a further volley, to make a dash for it and find safety.

Later that same afternoon, Corizis was captured, and two days after that Martin had an interview with him. It had been he, as Martin well knew, who had been behind the wall and who had shot Philsby. He was, as Martin put it, "stark mad and personally polite." He admitted that he had heard that Martin and Philsby were in Athens and that he had wished to kill them.

"Why?" Martin asked. "What harm had we ever done to you?"

"None whatsoever, personally," said this young man. "Rather the reverse. But I've come to hate all that stable way of life in which I was brought up—to hate it and to want to see it destroyed—to want to see it destroyed in everything, and even in myself, and I could not be absolutely sure that I had utterly killed it in myself until I had killed my friends. After a little practise it's very easy to kill people you've never seen before, and it's more than easy to kill one's enemies. But no one can be really sure of his faith until he has steeled himself to kill his friends. I used rather to like Philsby. He used to be quite good-looking at school, in a lazy, sleepy sort of way. That's why I got such a kick out of killing him."

Martin protested against such talk.

"Oh, it's no good being narrow-minded about such things," said the young man, "and pretending that we are other than we are. One must explore all the potentialities of human nature."

Martin asked why he was not shot, too.

"Partly, because you were too quick for us," said Corizis. "Partly, because I had a peculiar whim. My whim was to take you prisoner and then carry you up to the top of Parnassus and crucify you there. I have, you see, odd, degraded, sentimental memories of the school chapel, that big east window over the altar and, somehow or other—well, somehow or other, it seemed the right plan to crucify you. One should always do violence to these sentimental memories. It is necessary to eradicate them by some obscenity. If not, they remain on to weaken one."

Then, Martin said, this strange pervert went on to describe in truly beautiful and sincere language the view from the top of Lycorea: "The time to see it is just before sunrise. In clear weather you can see right over Euboea to the Northern Sporades to the east, up to Athos to the north-east, and to Olympus to the north, and south-east right down to Attica and to the sea beyond, and south over to the Peloponnese and to the mountains of Northern Arcadia. Then, as the sun rises, the more distant prospect becomes gradually blurred, but, instead, all the lakes and rivers of the plains of Phokis and Boeotia are picked out one by one by the sun, and gleam and sparkle like a distant town at evening when the lights go up. July is the best month for that view. Before July there is still too much snow about, and the sun is not yet quite strong enough to give the snow its full effect. After July there is apt to be a bit of mist in the air."

Martin learnt afterwards that Corizis had been taken because his men had turned against him. These men were simple, decent murderers. Some had joined him through desire to fight the Germans in the days when his movement was still a resistance movement. Some were of left-wing political opinions and had joined for what are known as ideological reasons. Some were brigands who had joined for loot, or, at least, men who had been driven to brigandage by the alternative of starvation. Some—perhaps the majority—had joined simply because it was in the Greek tradition, dating right back to the Klepths and the War of Independence, to join up, when there was a war on, with an irregular force which preyed impartially on both belligerents. But none, toughs as they may have been, shared Corizis' peculiar taste for blood. They were intelligent enough to see that that taste, if it could not be satisfied otherwise, might well be satisfied on his own followers. They had lived on into a world in which cannibalism was beginning to come back into fashion, and they knew, too, that murdering British officers was a dangerous game that was likely, in the end, to bring its own retribution. Therefore, they turned on their own leader. They betrayed him. As one of them put it to Martin, they "turned Conservative—what you call, 'crossed the floor of the house,' " he said, wiping some blood off from between his fingers with a dirty rag.

Don't you see how shattering all this has been to Martin—I do not mean physically—I mean morally? Pitchforked out of this genial, easy-going world, in which

> There's so much bad in the best of us
> And so much good in the worst of us,

he suddenly comes face to face with evil as a hideous, positive, terrifying force, comes face to face with the challenge to which he had, up till then, been unduly and immaturely blind: that this rampant evil is not the denizen of odd corners and obscene lunatic asylums, but that it may, if we are not brave and careful, prove itself to be the strongest force in the modern world. Don't you see that he is frightened? Don't you see that he does very well to be frightened?

Do you remember how, in the May before the war,

Bobby and you and I went to Orvieto? We drove up there from Perugia over the high ridge between the Tiber and the Chiuna and past the oak woods and the scented broom which was already in full, golden flower. And, in the cathedral, do you remember Signorelli's frescoes? The Four Last Things. And, above all, the preface to them, the Coming of Antichrist. Antichrist in that fresco is no dreadful monster, but a grand and beautiful figure with more than a suggestion about him of his Antitype. He is surrounded by other figures as dignified as himself and by objects of beauty and luxury. At first sight there seems to be no wickedness here—only worldliness—until you look into Antichrist's eyes, where you see the light of wickedness that comes from beyond the world, and then, in the background, behind all that is comfortable and all that is orderly, you see the picture of the persecutions and the bloodshed which are the end of these things. Is not that the whole history of the world in our lifetime, beginning with an enlightened secularism, which looks as if it was much the same as Christianity, only rather more sensible, and ending with a gospel that comes from beyond this world as patently as Christianity does, but which comes as patently from hell—a gospel which uses indifferently the little secular faiths of left and right, in which foolish men imagine that they put their faith, and which knocks their heads together for its sport?

Love, Peter

49

My dear,

Of course I see that it is as difficult for you as it was for Martin to believe that the conventionally naughty, laughing schoolboy, whom you remember coming to tea at Trumpinghurst, has turned out this extraordinary figure, like something repulsive out of the most melodramatic of Russian novels. That is just the difficulty. It is like the argument for miracles *à rebours*. The evidence that miracles have happened at, say, Lourdes is overwhelming. People who have not seen them reject them, because the demand on their imagination is too great. So, too, with these eruptions of perversion which appear in such times as ours, when the crust of civilisation has been broken through.

But in each particular case there is always a particular story. *Nemo fuit repente turpissimus*, and so with Corizis. He first fled up into the mountains straightforwardly to escape the Germans. For a time, he was one of those drawing-room resisters who were quite common in the early days of German occupation—always attending women's tea-parties in Athens with a pistol ostentatiously protruding from his pants and saying: "You really must excuse me now, darling. I have to be off to the mountains." Then they trapped him into murdering a German, and his pal, who was in on the killing, was captured and squealed on him. So he had burnt his boats. After that, he had to start robbing Greeks in order to get food, and, before long, in a scuffle there, he killed a Greek. Thus it went on, with freedom slowly broadening from precedent to precedent, each particular step in the downward path intelligible, the whole cumulative effect horrible.

I've seen some reports now about the state of affairs in Greece which you should understand if you are to pass judgment on them. Do you know that up in the Epirus mountains there are boys and girls whose parents have been killed, living by cannibalism on one another and on those whom they find, with no clothes at all, unable to speak any language at all, able only to make animal noises like hungry wolves? Is it not a bit premature to ask of such people whether they are National Liberals or Independent Liberals?

The way really to understand an age is, I think, to read an outstandingly great artist of another age, who saw the great problems of the former age *sub specie aeternitatis*, ignorant of the details by which judgment is so easily clouded. Of course—to speak seriously—if we would understand our age, we must know the details of it, the news that is in the newspapers and the news that is not in the newspapers. But it is also necessary to read a great artist through, with whom you can stand back from the picture and see it in perspective, and, as the interpreter of our age, my money is on Dostoievsky.

There is only one novelist whom I myself could put into the small class of baker's dozen of writers who really

184

matter—put right up into the class of Dante and Shakespeare and Aeschylus, and that is Dostoievsky. Trollope and Jane Austen and Balzac and plenty more are well worth having, but they do not quite make the top grade of all. Dostoievsky alone does that, and I can never understand why there is not more fuss about him. If the Conservative party ever seriously wants to get back to power, it ought to be reading him and quoting him and learning him by heart, and never let him out of its sight, and still less out of its head, from morning till night. For, Dostoievsky was the first person to spot that all these modern libertarian movements, wherever they might intend to end, must, in fact, inevitably end in absolute tyranny. Any fool can see that now, but it required a pretty powerful genius to see it in the 1870s, when the movements still only existed on paper. You get this in a sort of parable in *The Brothers Karamazov*. You get it directly and explicitly in *The Possessed*—in the account of the meeting of the revolutionaries in Virginsky's house. The others do not like Shigalev, but they have no answer to him, any more than the later revolutionaries of reality were to have an answer to Lenin. "Starting from unlimited freedom, I arrive at unlimited despotism," he says. "I will add, however, that there can be no solution of the social problem but mine." "He suggests," explains the lame man, "as a final solution of the question, the division of mankind into two unequal parts. One-tenth enjoys absolute liberty and unbounded power over the other nine-tenths. The others have to give up all individuality and become, so to speak, a herd and, through boundless submission, will, by a series of regenerations, attain primeval innocence, something like the Garden of Eden." The two basic points, I should say, in Dostoievsky were: (1) Unless liberty is valued as a good in itself, it does not survive. (2) It can only be valued as a good in itself, if the problem is approached theologically. He not only insisted on the universal fact of original sin, but also on the very common fact of satanic possession, and believed in both quite literally. The "possessed"—the revolutionaries—are explicitly compared to the Gadarene swine. Do read him, darling; I don't believe that you ever have. You are always catching me out about books. It is such fun to catch you out for once.

Love, Peter

P. S. Talking of Jane Austen, is it not, by the way, about time that someone said that Jane Austen was a bad writer?—not, of course, that the opinion would be true or even sensible, but it is the one thing left in the world that nobody ever has said. Princes and thrones, churches and creeds, systems and philosophies, and all the great masters of them, all have been debunked in this iconoclastic age. Even I have dared to say that Nat Gubbins was not funny. There is only one thing at which, up to the present, everyone has drawn the line. No one has dared to say that Jane Austen could not write.

50

My dear,

There does seem to me all the difference in the world between Margaret's case and Martin's. I do not know that I bother very much about the ordinary prudential arguments against early marriages in such times as these. I am in favour of early marriages at the best of times and rather against prudence in marriage—that is to say, excessive prudence. A prudent marriage—that is to say, a provident, a forward-looking, marriage—is a contradiction in terms. Marriage is of its nature an imprudent thing, a plunge, a gamble, a venture into the unknown, and no marriages are less successful than those which are delayed until the couple think that they can marry without the smallest material inconvenience. But in any event these arguments are for normal times. What pertinence have they to-day when prudence of that sort is in itself the highest form of folly? What sense is there to-day in saying to the young, "Wait another year or two until you have saved a little money," when obviously it is just as likely that in another year or two they will have lost all the money that they have now got?

I remember very well the Brown Mat at Eton saying, many years ago: "Man in his first origins was nomadic. The beginning of civilisation is the settled home."

I little thought that we should live to see the return of nomadic man, live to see men and women by the million wandering over the face of the earth with no home or country to which they can return, and, most of them, with rapidly diminishing chances of ever finding such a home. And all the institutions of civilisation are so tied up with the settled home that it is indeed a great question what can be preserved, or what ought to be preserved, in this brave, new nomadic world.

Marriage, for instance. How can you have marriage in the full sense without a settled home? And, if you cannot have it, what ought you to do about it? A lot of people in practise, and some people in theory, think that the only thing to do is to abolish it—to go back to free love. But the answer to free love, surely, is that it does not exist. The essence of love is the desire to bind oneself. It will be time enough to talk about free love when you can abolish jealousy by Act of Parliament. It is all very well to argue that you should be allowed to change your wife as easily as you change your house and that scientific birth-control can see to it that the problem is not complicated by unwanted children, but it is not as easy as all that.

"Indeed, it isn't," says Michael, who, sometimes, from his Disraelian aloofness from society is able to see the more clearly its comicalities. "It is perfectly easy to change your wife these days, but quite impossible to change your house without getting permits from four Government Departments, and, if you want to marry a new wife, there is no difficulty at all about getting rid of the three whom you already possess, but every difficulty about getting a permit to buy some utility furniture."

But all this is straying a long way from your children, none of whom have as yet even been divorced—let alone, married—and the great distinction that I would draw there between Margaret's and Martin's situation is this: Obviously, there is no way of stopping Margaret from marrying Michael, and why should you want to? She reminds me exactly of you in the days when we used to ride together over the Kentucky Blue Grass.

Thou art thy mother's glass, and she in thee
Calls back the lovely April of her prime.

Is that a compliment or a stab? Her's is a genuine case, but Martin seems in my judgment to be an entirely different kettle of fish. That is not love, but curiosity. He wants to discover what all this is about. After Greece and Africa and battle and murder and sudden death, he wants to come home—a laudable ambition. He wants Somerset and Barston and the hay and the harvest and "the church clock at ten to three," and "honey still for tea" and all that that implies. And two of the things that that implies are a wife sitting on the other side of the fire in winter and noisy, horrible children to be bowled to in summer. Excellent, but his mistake is in tagging all that on to this particular young lady on the principle of first come, first served. He is not in love with her at all, but he is in love with love, and, if he tells you that he ought to marry, the answer is that certainly he ought to marry—somebody else—reasonably soon, but not in too great a hurry. If he

189

won't take it from you or from me, then tell him to take it from Shakespeare. Tell him to read *Romeo and Juliet*. The best touch in that play is that Romeo starts it off in love, as he imagines, with "fair Rosaline." The truth was that he was ready to be in love before he met Juliet, and, therefore, Rosaline had to fill in for a time as an understudy. There is no need for us to play Benvolio. Juliet will come along soon enough without our help.

If he must read love poetry, then let him—at this juncture, at any rate—read hard, metaphysical, rationalist stuff about what love is—Dante, for instance, or, if not him, Donne—not all this romantic stuff with Tit-Willow dons a-sighing and a-sobbing. I rather like Housman in some moods—taken with onions—but it is dangerous for the young who may still believe him.

> *When I was one-and-twenty*
> *I heard a wise man say*
> *"Give crowns and pounds and guineas*
> *But not your heart away.*
> *Give pearls away and rubies*
> *But keep your fancy free";*
> *But I was one-and-twenty,*
> *No use to talk to me.*
>
> *When I was one-and-twenty*
> *I heard him say again,*
> *"The heart out of the bosom*
> *Was never given in vain*
> *'Tis paid with sighs a plenty*
> *And sold for endless rue."*

And I am two-and-twenty
And oh, 'tis true, 'tis true.

On which I comment:

When I was two-and-twenty
He said it all once more.
He said it all so often,
He was a frightful bore.
I came to think such nonsense
The damnedest stuff alive
When talked by dons of sixty
To boys of twenty-five.

Love, Peter

51

June 29, 1945.

My dear,

Of course, and obviously, you must vote for Michael. It seems to me that the Liberals are completely cracky, and, if they have a policy, it is quite certain that neither Michael nor, so far as I can see, any other Liberal candidate agrees with it. In any event, I don't suppose that he has one chance in a million of getting in, so, what harm? But things would have come to a pretty pass, indeed, if you were to allow political principle to come before private friendship.

To be honest, I cannot pretend to understand this party politics business. It is just a little bit too dotty for my liking. If one says anything serious or sensible about it, one is accused either of being excruciatingly witty or wickedly cynical. For instance, the whole lesson of history is surely that there are two conditions necessary for the successful working of parliamentary government: (1) that there shall be two parties, and not more than two; (2) that there shall be no difference between them. The fight can then be confined purely to personalities, as it ought to be—to the question which team will best carry out the agreed policy. If there is a fundamental difference on policy, then it is obvious that affairs are reduced to a deadlock. You cannot nationalise the mines and denationalise them every five years. You cannot have the Stuarts in one election and the Hanoverians in the next and so on *ad infinitum*. These things have to be settled one way or the other.

Well, never was there a time, one would have thought, when these conditions for good government were more manifestly present than to-day. The leaders of the parties have sat amicably together in Cabinet for the last five years. The Conservatives are so socialist and the Socialists are so conservative that, really, it is quite beyond the wit of man to remember which is which. I, in my old age, should rather like to see less state interference and less general beveridging about, but no one can pretend that there is the smallest reason to think that there would be less of it under a Conservative Government. So, in such a world, there are only two things to be done —either to go on with a National Government, or, if you want to have party politics, then just vote against a man because you don't like his face. But, if that is so, then why must they be so rude to one another? Can't they see that they are cutting their own throats by doing so? The division in English politics to-day is not between those who are Conservatives and those who are Socialists. The division is between those who think the game of party politics worth preserving (and who incidentally are, as the case may be, either Conservatives or Socialists) and those who do not think it worth preserving. If the politicians behave like clowns, they do not damage their opponents; they damage their whole profession, and, if they are not very careful, will, as Robert so epigrammatically put it, "upset the whole bloody apple-cart." And it is, very seriously, a pity, because it would have been a most wonderful example to all the world, if they could have kept their whole campaign on a dignified and moderate plane.

It is always thought a joke or a cynicism to say that it is of the essence of party politics that each party should contain a good deal of the spirit of the other party. It is, of course, in reality, a truism. You remember what Huey Long said to us at Baton Rouge eleven years ago, not so very long before they shot him. He said: "Any fool can start a fascist party. All you have to do is to call it an anti-fascist party." He was wickedly cynical but a diabolically able man, and I think that it is the complete summary of the history of the last eleven years since it was said. By a parallel reasoning I would say: "It is child's play to stop socialism. All you have to do is to elect a Labour Government." And that, I think, is perfectly true, provided that "the whole bloody apple-cart" does not collapse. Socialism, in the peroration, is often idealist and liberal and international, but the only sort of socialism that has ever worked is national socialism—whether in Germany or in Russia. But, whatever survives the next years, the present party divisions certainly will not survive, so I do not know that I take them very seriously.

Love, Peter

52

July 3, 1945.

My dear,

George tells me that it is very wrong of me not to take party politics seriously. He tells me that the Conservatives are all right and the Socialists are all wrong (or perhaps it was the other way round. I am not quite sure, like Saki's young lady, who knew the difference between right and wrong, but never could remember which was which). Anyway, it all matters tremendously, and parliamentary government is very important and only fools jeer at the forms of it—says George.

I am inclined to think that he is right about parliamentary government and that everybody thinks the forms of it ridiculous at first sight, but after a time comes to see them as important. On parties I think that Belloc's analysis, allowing for exaggeration, was essentially right. The two parties are and must be much less different than they pretend. But Belloc was wrong in thinking that a fraudulent plan. It is an obviously sensible and, indeed, necessary plan.

How I hate people who do not go regularly to church! I speak from experience, as I did not go near one myself for many years. But lack of church-going is so vulgar, and you can see the vulgarity stamped on the faces of the non-goers. It is like being tone-deaf and boasting of it. And so, to compare great things with small, I think that sneering at the ritual of parliamentary government is cheap and probably vulgar. Parliamentary government with all its faults is at any rate a great deal better than non-parliamentary government. *Peccavi, mea culpa.* But, at the same time, I am still a little puzzled by the frequency of concerted conspiracy among parliamentarians to say exactly the opposite of the truth about things.

Take, for instance, the mines. I have just been up spending a week-end with the admirable Johnstone, who is resting between his labours and the declaration of his victory, so I am rather well up in this. If you went to political meetings, you would think that there are Socialists clamouring for nationalisation and Conservatives defending free enterprise and saying that the state must not poke its nose into a mine. Actually, when you examine the Socialist scheme of nationalisation and the sort of reorganisation which the Conservatives would put through under the Reid Report, you find that there is not much difference between them. I do not say that there is no difference, but not very much. Actually, it seems to me, and Johnstone quite agrees with me, that the people who stand to gain out of nationalisation are the mine-owners. Mines are not good investments. Whatever government may be in power, mine-owning is never again going to be owning in any normal sense of the word. Therefore, if they get tolerable compensation, they are lucky to be out of it. On the other hand, the prospect for the trade union leaders, as Johnstone frankly admits, is far from rosy. The main cause of the decline in output is absenteeism, and miners refuse to go down the mines, not because they dislike the mines' being owned by private capitalists, but because they dislike going down mines. Johnstone himself thinks that things will be rather better after nationalisation and rather better if some modern improvements are introduced, but he does not kid himself that they will be very much better. On the other hand, the owners are very useful to the union leaders now as whipping boys. The blame can be put on them, when anything goes wrong, though usually they have nothing to do with it. After nationalisation we shall have to take the rap, said Johnstone. It is an irony that workers' control should be coming just when it is meaningless—when the workers have ceased to think of their elected leaders as workers any more. I asked him whether, under nationalisation, strikes would be forbidden. "They will be forbidden," he said, "but I should not wonder if they would be more common than ever." He is a very refreshing man. They are grand men—the best of the trade union leaders—so hard-headed, so free from illusion, and so fond of beer.

Love, Peter

53

August 15, 1945.

My dearest,

Do, please, be kind. Of course, I know all too well how much justification there is in your charge of idleness. I am a dilettante inveterate, and a smack of metaphysics is the easiest and most insidious of all invitations to indolence. It is so fatally tempting to say: "Of course, I should love to get up and do something about it, if only I could feel sure that my actions would be of any benefit.

But, really, truth and the future are so uncertain, so many of the things that human beings do are harmful rather than beneficial, and had much better have been left undone, that it is safer to turn over on my other side and go to sleep." I confess freely enough that I have sinned all too often. Whatever my other faults, I at least have never been backward in confession.

Yet, even sinners may apologise, and may I say what I think I can fairly say for myself? There are two types of mind—what I may call the pragmatic and the metaphysical. I won't indulge in any Aristotelian jeers at *banausia* and claim that the latter is in any way superior to the former—particularly not, when found in such very debased and minor form as I may claim to possess it. I merely say that they are different. There are chaps—and many of them both very much more intelligent and very much better than I am—who find it easy simply to by-pass the ultimate mysteries. Nothing within them compels them to ask the final questions, and they are able to throw themselves whole-heartedly into causes, and to work for the purposes of parties without tormenting themselves continually with *"Cui bono"* and "Will people be any better if all this is done?"

> *Lay thou on for Tusculum*
> *And I'll lay on for Rome,*

and the Roman—such a Roman—does not find it at all strange that the Tuscan lays on for Tusculum. He would think it unnatural if he did not. Neither are they tormented with deep questions, and such people are in many ways much to be envied, and it is a very good thing for the world that many of them exist.

But the world has also its Hamlets—some of them, like myself, very minor and ineffective Hamlets, but Hamlets *malgré nous*. Some people bother about the freedom of the will, and some people don't bother. But, whatever the limits of freedom, there is one thing about which we certainly are not free: we are not free to bother or not to bother about freedom. There, at any rate, we are as we are. A chap like David, for instance, is a very able fellow —and also a very honourable fellow. He goes on working away at his politics and his business, and doing very useful work at them, too. If you were to ask him if he were a Christian, he would reply, "Of course," thinking that he meant that he was not a Jew. If you pressed him and asked him again if he believed in Christianity, he would reply, "Oh, yes," thinking that you meant, "Did he believe in attending regularly at the County Council and not cheating over the change, even if he had a chance to?" But, if you pressed him about the details of his belief, about the reconciliation of some of the apparent contradictions, he simply would not know what you were talking about, one way or the other, any more than I should know what Professor Einstein was talking about if he expounded to me the details of relativity. I do not sneer at that. There is a lot to be said for not bothering about questions that cannot be answered and for getting on with the job. But saying has nothing much to do with it one way or the other. Hamlet did not find it any particular fun being Hamlet. He just could not help himself, and people who are made metaphysical cannot help being metaphysical. That is all that I would plead. Every type of character has its own peculiar temptations, and I make no claim to have invariably resisted my temptations. But it is useless to complain that I am what I am, for that I cannot help. It is useless to complain that, while others can give their whole-hearted energy to raising the standard of living, I tend, rather, to wonder whether those with high standards of living are better or happier than those with low. It is useless to complain that, when others bring out, undoubting, the broom of moral reformation, I wonder, rather, how much that passes for virtue is really virtue, and how much that passes for vice is really vice.

Sorry, my dear, but that's the sort of chap I am. I love Dante, I love Shakespeare, I love Pascal, but there was also Swift and there was also Montaigne, and he who has been set asking questions by the Montaignes can never, willy-nilly, rest unquestioning again. Sometimes he wishes to God that he could, but he cannot.

Now, there is about your children a pleasant Rabelaisian earthiness, through grace of which they can, I hope, venture on the intellectual voyages without risk of falling victim to the sceptic's pessimism, and at the same time enough theology in them to save them from the danger of Rabelais. Only very good theologians should read Rabelais. I see that now. His was the most attractive and, therefore, the most dangerous of all the heresies—the simple invitation to love life, to throw off all restraint, and all would be well—that invitation put out, not in some dry Pelagian treatise, but by "the quintessentially regalian lips" themselves, by the great lover of Thelême. Who could stand against it?

Well, of course, as a philosophy,

> *And is it true? It isn't true,*
> *And, if it were, it wouldn't do.*

It just is not so. There is Original Sin. It is very inconvenient, but there it is. If a person knows that, then there is no harm in his reading Rabelais. There is no harm in the world in anyone taking Rabelais as a recreation, as long only as there is no danger of his taking him as a philosophy. And that is why your children are so lucky, and why I approve so much of their coarseness and earthiness and bad language, and why anyone would be a fool who tried to check it. "Thy greatest knew thee, Mother Earth," as Meredith said, and coarseness is the revelation of a sudden glory, if it is combined with the firm hold on wisdom, and that is where your children are so lucky. They have inherited the firm hold—inherited it in such a way that they could not divest themselves of it, even if they wished to do so. You remember Browning's apologia for Aristophanes.

God bless you, my dear. I hope that you do not mind my rambling on like this, but rambling is a form of admiration.

Love, Peter

54

My dear Ruth,

How did Barston celebrate the defeat of Japan? With us in London I fear that the war went out with a whimper. Partly, that was because the government sprang VJ-Day on the public without notice. But I doubt if, in any event, there would have been much heart in celebrations. I dined alone with David at the club. It was a fantastic performance. The staff, naturally enough, was depleted in the day's honour, and the question was whether there was anybody who could bring us two cups of coffee. In the end, we unearthed a young urchin, a sort of Elizabethan scullion, who could not, indeed, bring coffee himself, but who might be able to tell somebody else who might be able to bring some. Then the next three-quarters of an hour was filled with this urchin's popping in and out with the latest news. "It's coming." "No, it isn't coming." "Yes, it's coming." It was just like the rumours and counter-rumours about the Japanese surrender, and then, like the Japanese surrender, in the end it came—and was, I need hardly say, stone-cold.

I think that it is the atomic bomb which has for the moment flattened people out. It surely knocks out completely any case that we may ever have had for trying war criminals. Justice cannot claim to be justice unless it is impartial. I do not suppose that there was anyone in the world before 1939 who would not have said an atomic bomb was an illegitimate weapon. *Ergo*, if we try anybody else for war crimes, we must, if we are going to pretend that we are doing justice, also try those who were responsible for its dropping.

I cannot understand why they dropped it. The excuses given out are all fantastically inadequate. There was, as far as I can make out, no suggestion that the Japanese were preparing to drop one—no reason to think, even, that we would not win the war without it. The only excuse is that it would shorten the war. But this is precisely the excuse which Goebbels made for bombing Coventry. No one in all history has ever been so mad as to commit an atrocity which he did not think would be effective, and, on that excuse, one can clearly excuse anything.

The trouble about atomic bombs and suchlike seems to me to be that, in the long run, they must inevitably put all the power into the hands of the least free country in the world. Through the centuries we in England have been able to preserve some liberty and to save England by our exertions and Europe by our example through our geographical advantage. Behind the moat of the Channel we have been able to be peacetime-minded in peace. That has meant that, when the war came, we were always unprepared for it and lost all the battles for the first few years. The Opposition of the day stormed at the Government of the day, and sometimes the Opposition of the day became the Government and lost a few battles in its turn.

But, inconvenient as these defeats were, we could afford them. Time was on our side, and we were able to win in the end. Time was even still on our own side in 1940— only just—only by the skin of our teeth—but still we did pull through. But now it will never be on our side again. In future wars we shall not have three years to play with. We shall not have three seconds to play with. The country which hesitates for five minutes of debate, for five minutes of consultation of public opinion, will be beaten to the draw by the nation that can entirely neglect such consideration.

Of course, people say that the answer is to bring these weapons under international control. Such formulae may prove to have some meaning. Let us hope that they will. But, as long as everybody is inveterately national-minded, it is very difficult to see how phrases about inter-national control can be more than phrases, and few people are very sanguine about the outcome. The people I meet are almost unanimous in their pessimism—don't you find people so? But, what is odder still, they are all complacent in their pessimism—Don't you find that, too? Presump-tion and despair are twin sisters. Quite a few years ago people tended to be absurdly over-optimistic about the attainment of Utopia—quite a few simple legislative changes, and all the problems of the world would be settled and we would all live happily ever after. Now they have swung round to the exact opposite. They agree, without question, that it is highly unlikely that the organ-isation of the United Nations will succeed. They agree, without question, that these first atomic bombs, that kill, it seems, a mere matter of some 70,000 people, are but children's models, and that in a few years' time the course of progress will enable us to annihilate a continent as easily as we can annihilate a city or our ancestors could annihilate a bumble-bee. But—and this is the curious thing—they mind very little. I have yet to come across anybody who is willing to go on record as saying that it would be a bad thing that the world should be destroyed. This is, indeed, a curious comment on a hundred and fifty years of secularism and progress and belief in perfectibility, beginning with a dawn in which it was bliss to be alive, and to be young was very heaven, ending with a dark night in which shivering men pray for death, lacking even the faith that will give them hope that such a prayer will be attended. In all the centuries of Christian sorrow one certainly comes across no despair such as that of these songs before a sunrise which no man any longer expects to see. What ought one to do about it? Or ought one to do anything about it? Perhaps they are right.

Love, Peter

55

August 29, 1945.

My dear,

It is a great sign of grace in you that you are able to be depressed. Most people these days are, I find, beneath pessimism. They agree with me on the probabilities of annihilation, but do not mind, since Nothing is better than Anything. But I am sure that the answer is that we must stop being too clever by half, we must stop acting on the maxim that the end justifies the means—we must understand that things are now in such a mess that it is no good bothering too much about looking to consequences. No one can tell what the consequences may be. We must take a dose of *"Fiat justitia, ruat coelum."*

Take the question of humanity and these beastly ideologies. The decent tradition surely is that here is a man who is starving or in distress, therefore you help him. The modern tradition is that you first start by asking whether he is a fascist or a communist or something, and then, if it turns out that he is of the wrong ideology, you either say that he is a liar who is just pretending that he is starving, or that it serves him right to starve, or that it is sentimentalism to feed one's enemies or some other equally delectable observation. Well, even on the pragmatic plane, that has not turned out so well. Things are not very beautiful in the garden, and we could hardly do worse if

206

we tried, instead, a policy of decency for decency's sake
—wherever there was a man or woman starving or in want,
relieve him, if we could, simply because he or she was a
human being, and without stopping to ask whether the
human being was Jew or Gentile, black or white, Catholic
or Protestant, communist or fascist. It is just possible that,
if we did that, we might even yet rescue the tottering
apple-cart—that to forget about policy might prove to be
the best policy—and that, just as people have become more
ideological by always talking about ideologies, so they
might become less ideological by the very fact of not
talking about ideologies. Even if it is too late now to save
things, and we are doomed to go down the drain, it is
better to go down the drain with decency than without it.

Love, Peter

56

September 2, 1945.

My dear,

Of course, in one way all this writing is a very odd
business. There are forty million people in this country,
and I forget how many hundred million in the world, and

multiply that by heaven knows how many for the number of generations that have lived and died since time began and, when a man has done all that sum, how can he imagine that his contribution to the world's knowledge or the world's beauty can be original? It always amazes me that a man should even be able to churn out sentences and phrases that are not identical word for word with those which, as far as record goes, have been used before, but real originality of thought is clearly all but an impossibility. If new, it can hardly be true, and, if true, it can hardly be new. Of course, you may say that the style is the thing, and that each generation has to find its new ways of saying the old things. I think that that is true. But, even if we allow that that brings down the odds a bit, still it remains extraordinary that anyone should have the impudence to challenge the bookies and think that such random thoughts as may flit through his brain are deserving of publication.

And I often wonder why it is that they do it. Perhaps there are geniuses—men who are the children of a special inspiration, and who know that they are such—men who know that the merely mathematical odds are irrelevant to them and that, in defiance of all apparent probability, they can build the

> *monumentum aere perennius*
> *quod non imber edax, non Aquilo impotens*
> *possit diruere aut innumerabilis*
> *anorum series . . .*

(Is not Horace good? I remember that one of the beaks

at Eton used to say that he was "not quite tip-top" as a poet. What a fool!) Anyway, let us count out geniuses who, perhaps, are as they are and cannot help themselves. There remain the enormous number of writers—and artists of every sort—who are not frightfully good, that is, exceptionally good, and know that they are not. Why do they do it? I don't mean, why do they write? To write—to draw—to sing—these seem to me perfectly natural, normal activities, just like laughing. I can very well see that everybody wants to express himself in one way or another. The abnormality would be not to wish to do so. But it is publishing that is the mystery. No one wants to publish his laugh. Why does he want to publish his poems?

I think that there must be some curious psychological explanation—a sort of sublimation of the desire for children in some strange way. I do not say that, because strange, it is, therefore, disreputable. But it is odd.

Love, Peter

57

My dear,

Margaret came to see me yesterday, fresh back from Ireland, and I am so glad to find that she has stood up to it pretty well—all except the aeroplane, and I can well imagine that that must have been foul, with the wind bucketing as it did yesterday. But she was well enough to come dining round the town with me in the evening with a charming Australian Labour M.P. whom we had picked up, nobody could quite remember how. We finished up, in the House of Commons, in the tow of Tony and the never-sufficiently-to-be-loved Mr. Johnstone. When "Who Goes Home" came, this lovely Australian started to sing "Land of Hope and Glory" in the lobby, and the policeman came up to stop him. The Australian's attitude was perfect. Being a guest and a man of infinite courtesy, he did not take it on himself to push the policeman's face in, but he assumed that his two hosts would do this for him. The notion that no face would be pushed in at all, that two Members of Parliament—one Labour and one Conservative—would weakly allow their guest to be stopped singing in the Palace of Westminster by a policeman exceeded his wildest dreams of tyranny. Yet this—needless to say—was what happened. It was a fascinating lesson in what different people mean by a free country.

Perhaps Australia is the only free country left in the world. I never was there.

It is a great advantage to be, like Margaret, engaged to be married to an English Catholic. For the English Catholics are, as a general rule, by common repute, of all people the most impervious to Irish romance. Not that Michael is prejudiced. He seems to be the most unprejudiced of people on religion or on anything else—with few prejudices in favour of his co-religionists and no prejudices against them. However, his important role in Margaret's Irish visit was that of not being there, and it was his absence which guarded her from the temptation of looking at Ireland too romantically.

Well, my dear, I congratulate you on your daughter. I have often done so before, and I do so now again. She seems to have steered admirably between the Scylla of complaining that Ireland is not exactly like England and the Charybdis of romanticising it just because it is different. The Lovegroves are Protestants and what used to be called Unionists and Anglo-Irish and Ascendancy and all that. But do not for one moment imagine that they are, therefore, Englishwomen or in the least like Englishwomen. Of course, in their heart of hearts they think the worse of Sean O'Donovan because he did not kill the policeman. From that day forward Sean has always been thought of as a vaguely contemptible and comic figure by everyone in Ireland, whatever her politics, and will be so thought of until his death. And why? In the last analysis, for no other reason than that he was sent to kill the policeman and, when he got there, played cards with him instead. And this, in Irish eyes, is so contemptible a thing to have done that the accident that he is, I believe, one of the most efficient and honest administrators in the country weighs not a jot against it.

Or take Father O'Flaherty. You would not find, I grant you, many Anglican vicars who would bawl at you from their front porches at half-past eleven in the morning to come into their house, who would fill you up with three large whiskies, who would know backwards the form of every horse in England and Ireland, and, if you did find such a man in England, you would think him a wordly fellow and call him with a sneer a sporting parson, and probably you would be right. But such a sporting parson in England would be very unlikely to know almost by heart the *Summa* of St. Thomas and the novels of Balzac and to spend, I daresay, two hours a day, morning and night, in spiritual meditation. You may say that the contradictions of such a character are curious. Perhaps they are. I do not pretend that every priest in Ireland is like that, and, in any event, who am I to set myself up as an authority on curiosity? But I merely say that there it is—an Irish phenomenon. Do not pass upon it a superficial judgment. Do not think that the religion is insincere because it is fronted with a Rabelaisianism that is surprising to you, any more than it is insincere in many other Irishmen in whom it is fronted with a puritanism that is, perhaps, even more surprising to you. Ireland is the only country in the world that has had a conservative revolution—conservative, not in the superficial political sense, but in the fundamental metaphysical sense. In morals and religion and respect for tradition the Sinn Fein revolutionaries were far more conservative than the liberal-minded progressive Unionists, and Ireland, under Mr. de Valera, is to-day in many ways the last surviving relic of Victorian England—a country of stable morals and traditional beliefs in a shifting world. Here in Ireland is a different sort of animal. That is, perhaps, all that there is to it. Be humble and learn

> *For the great Gaels of Ireland*
> *Are the men whom God made mad,*
> *For all their wars are merry*
> *And all their songs are sad!*

Now, Margaret is quite admirable about all that. She has a sense that is rare indeed in the young, that there are separate types of excellence—that one goes to a foreign country neither to sneer nor to imitate, but to learn. As a general rule, among the young, travel narrows the mind. They come back from abroad too offensively John Bullish for words or else *inglese italianato*, but Margaret has a rare power of entering into the life at once on its own merits, driving round Dublin with that odd pal of hers in the absurd car with its door flapping open, playing tennis at the Lamberts' with pigs and hens running all over the court, climbing up into St. Kevin's bed at Glendalough—and taking it all in her stride, as the most natural thing in the world to do—something neither to be sneered at nor rudely praised, but to be accepted as a part of life. It is the rarest and most valuable of gifts—this power to accept life as a stuff from which to learn and a pageant to observe.

Most of us try to impose our theories on the facts and to twist the facts to fit the theories, to impose the lesser thing upon the greater, and thus we make ourselves ridiculous. But there have been a few who could accept the pageant and the mysteries—could wonder and admire without too much haste to criticise. Chaucer, for one, and your daughter, Margaret, for another, and perhaps one or two more. You remember that "Absalom, that was jolly and gay," of the "Miller's Tale":

A very child he was, so God me save;
Wel could he leten blood, and clippe and shave
And make a chartre of lond, and a quittance.
In twenty manere could he trip and dance
(After the schole of Oxenforde tho)
And with his legges casten to and fro;
And playen songes on a small ribible,
Thereto he sang sometime a loud quinible
And as wel could he play on a giterne.
In al the town was brewhouse ne taverne
That he ne visited with his solas
There as that any gaillard tapstere was.

That is what the young ought to be like.

Eheu, fugaces, Postume, Postume,
Oh, for the years that are lost to me, lost to me.

What is a ribible? Isn't it a delicious word? I am sure that it cannot be anything nearly as nice as it sounds.

Love, Peter

58

My dear,

I was motoring along the Fosse Way yesterday, when I thought of something of which I had never thought before. It was not a very profound, and I can hardly think that it was an original, reflection. But, for what it was worth, I offer it. When we talk of Roman roads, we always talk of how old they are, of how they have fought and conquered the centuries, of how the camps and the cities and the men that they served have perished, and the men and the cities that came after them, and they alone remain. What is there left to-day of Maresbury or of the Roman mines beyond Charterhouse? Of the Charterhouse itself or of its cell by Greenore? Where are Arthur and Alfred, Lancelot and Guinevere, the old church of Ynyswitryn or the men that fell at Penselwood? "The wind has blown them all away," and yet the Fosse, that has seen them come and go, still runs straight as a die, down the hill to Shepton Mallet. But this, which is now the oldest thing in England, was once the newest thing in England. It is not true that

Before the Roman came to Rye or out to Severn strode
The rolling English drunkard made the rolling English
road.

215

There was no road before there was a Roman road, and, to the first Briton, what was remarkable about it was not that it was a Roman road, but that it was a road at all. The road came to him as the first symbol of the brotherhood of man, the first evidence that there was a bond between him and other men beyond the tribe, and it ran then, as it still runs to-day, over the hills and out of sight and far away, beyond sight and beyond experience, to the world beyond the world. Family trees have something of the same sort of moral as Roman roads. We are but links in a chain—a chain that stretches from infinity to infinity—and—here is the paradox and the fallacy of individualism—we are only truly ourselves when we recognise ourselves as links in a chain. When Richard III in Shakespeare begins saying, "I am myself alone," we know that he is coming to a bad end.

I had plenty of time to think about all this, because I ran out of petrol just this side of Stratton. I can never remember to get petrol in Bath.

Love, Peter

59

My dear,

These Nuremberg trials do make me a little sick, and what makes me sickest of all is that very few people even seem to understand what it is that one is sick about. They seem to think that one has some tender spot for Ribbentrop and is objecting to the trials because one has a personal objection to him and his pals getting it in the neck. No one would have shed many tears if we had read in the papers one morning that Ribbentrop and Goering had met the fate of Mussolini and Goebbels, but, as it is, something very much more important than their fate is at stake. What is at stake is, surely, the whole question whether this world, after the war, is to be built upon a rule of law or upon a travesty of law.

What are these people being tried for? I can perfectly well understand the trial of someone who has violated the customs of war—who has, say, tortured prisoners, but to try people for waging aggressive war is much more difficult. By what code has the waging of war been declared a crime? We are told that it became a crime when the nations signed the Kellogg Pact and repudiated war as an instrument of policy. I am not enough of a lawyer to know whether that argument is valid or not, but, if you will, let it pass. What are the consequences of it?

The last act of the League of Nations was to expel Russia for her attack on Finland in 1939. So, if the waging of aggressive war is a crime, there is at least a *prima facie* case that the Russians are criminals—and yet they are to appear at Nuremberg, not in the dock, but on the bench. I am not even quite sure about the atomic bomb. I think that in 1939 it would have been very difficult to find anyone who believed that there was such a thing as international law at all, and who would not have agreed that to drop an atomic bomb in the conditions in which it was dropped at Hiroshima was a violation of international law. As for atrocities and the maltreatment of prisoners— no doubt the record of Germans and Japanese is very much worse than that of any other people, but does anyone seriously suggest that only Germans and Japanese have been guilty?

Justice cannot claim to be justice unless it is impartial. If we could establish a tribunal which would try impartially everyone of every nationality against whom these charges could be brought, then we could claim to have established a system of international law. But, if we cannot do that, we are punishing people, not because they are criminals, but because they are beaten, and it would be much better if we confessed that we were shooting and imprisoning them because they were our enemies and did so frankly as an act of war. The best thing may be the establishment of a system of international law. The worst enemy of the establishment of such a system is a bogus travesty of law. It would be far, far better to confess that it is not yet possible to establish such a system, if that be the sad truth, than to establish a travesty of it.

What bearing, you may say, has all that got on your children? A great deal, my dear, and, to be precise, this: I do not, as you know, quarrel with their desire not to be preoccupied with politics. On the contrary, I applaud it, but this detachment carries with it a certain obligation. All the regular parties are almost bound, in the nature of things, to talk a good deal of nonsense, and anyone who attaches himself to any of the regular parties is bound to talk a good deal of nonsense too. One of the evils of to-day is that there are not enough detached, independent, tolerably educated people of integrity who can raise a quite disinterested clamour whenever anything too utterly obscene is proposed. It is my whim that that is what your children may be able to do. It won't do them any good, of course. After a short time they will find the task almost incredibly tedious. They will get little thanks and less understanding. They will meet with small success. But it is worth doing, and it is almost the only thing left in the world that is worth doing.

Love, Peter

60

My dear,

"Sleep also is a form of criticism," said the French dramatic critic after he had slept through the play. Do not be worried that your children are not interested in politics, so long as they are ready to do reasonable, decent, sensible things. Politics will come soon enough, if come they must. I read last night in some old letters of the eighteenth century, "Last Monday your father was at Mr. Payn's and plaid at cricket, and came home pleased enuf, for he struck the best båll in the game, and wished he had not anything else to do and would play at Cricket all his Life." How I agree! There are other things to do, of course, and they must be done, but do not jeer at people who are content to do the simple, small, immediate things. Like Candide, let us cultivate our garden, and then, when we have done that well, it will be time enough, perhaps, to go forward to greater things. I do not want them to be cynics, but I do want them to be satirists. So much that is praised as progress is, in truth, little more than the absence of satire. The world is not better than the world which Swift and Voltaire assailed. All that has happened is that it is no longer capable of producing writers like Swift and Voltaire to show how it is as bad.

Hatred, greed, pride in Candide's day were found
To be the laws by which the world went round.
It's much the same; for still pride, hatred, greed
Are all around, but where, O, where's Candide?

Meliora speremus.

Love, Peter